BEYOND THE WALLS · 2021

Beyond the Walls

New Writing from York St John University

2021

Valley Press

First published in 2021 by Valley Press
Woodend, The Crescent, Scarborough, YO11 2PW
www.valleypressuk.com

ISBN 978-1-912436-60-6
Cat. no. VP0181

Editorial copyright © York Centre for Writing 2021
Individual copyright © as credited 2021

Cover artwork by Seline Layla Duzenli.
'Beyond the Walls' illustration by Katy Rose.
Text design by Peter Barnfather.

Printed and bound in Great Britain by
Imprint Digital, Upton Pyne, Exeter.

Contents

Foreword

Whenever a writer sits down to turn their ideas into words, they are moving into a space of the unknown. No matter how well planned their notes might be, no matter how clear their imagination and their ideas, the translation of those gleaming, abstract thoughts into solid words always means stepping out into a place you sense but cannot see. The unknown, as childhood memories of darkness attest, can be terrifying. But writers understand that there is also something beautiful in resilience through that darkness—following the pen (or keyboard), word by word, until you find the way to make thought tangible, vibrant, surprising, and alive.

We have all had to endure more resilience than usual over this last year. *Beyond the Walls* feels at once more appropriate a title than ever (we have all, staff and students alike, been scattered far beyond the university, communicating through our ghostly images on screens) and less—after all, trapped inside for long stretches, it can feel as if we are constantly walking in circles, trapped within (and longing to be, even briefly, beyond) our own walls.

The poems, stories, and essays in this collection respond to the subject of resilience through the unknown in brilliant and unexpected ways—by way of the Covid-19 Pandemic, yes, but also by way of food rituals, of nightly news cycles, of relationships made abstract and sinister by our separation. But perhaps the greatest way this writing responds to resilience is in its very existence—the appearance, on a blank and solitary page, of somebody else's words to take us to some place new.

Sam Reese, March 2021

Preface

resilience
noun
the capacity to recover
quickly from difficulties

unknown
adjective
not known or familiar

York is a city that embodies both. It sits on land older than time, houses buildings that have survived all manner of tragedies and impossible situations, and the people that live here are survivors. York St. John is not much different. With a history that encourages adaptability and the promise of untold stories, it is no wonder the writers born within its walls are ready to break free and show the world what they are capable of. Though we look back and thank the history that brought us here, life is about living, and to do that we must move forward, to the future and all the uncharted waters that face us ahead. It may be scary, it may make us wish for the comfort of yesterday, but that is what makes it life. This anthology means to show us this, with the talent that York St. John University brings, given a voice by Valley Press, we take this time to look forward.

Let's journey *Beyond The Walls* together.

Student Editorial Team

Beyond
The
Walls

Moving Day

A. T Ainscough

For Terence, Saturdays used to be planned down to the finest detail. Before going to work, Julie would make scrambled eggs and bacon, which Terence would shove down his gullet ahead of beginning the manic rush of getting out the door in time to cart the kids off to their various clubs and activities. Then, Terence was a free man until five, as Julie would pick the kids up after her shift and take them to her parents', so she could whizz around Tesco before tackling the housework. For dinner, Terence would order everyone pizza, and he'd usually fall asleep before the kids.

This Saturday, Terence has a lie-in, which he utilises by failing to sleep, and instead stares at the ceiling, contemplating the uncertain road of the day. It feels like starting a sentence and then realising you don't speak the language, or getting ready to take a step before realising there is nowhere to go.

Terence thinks on this for so long that he becomes late to leave, though this doesn't prevent him stopping off for a quick McDonald's breakfast. Then, his throat scalded from gulping down his coffee too quickly, he goes to oversee the extradition of his belongings from the family home.

Terence makes a great show of directing the removal guys. He tells himself that, though different, this Saturday can still be productive. So, he offers help that is unwanted, waves his hands in vague imitation of someone directing a plane to land, and cringes when he sees the twitching net curtain from Mrs. Next Door. He hopes desperately that she will stay inside; he doesn't need to be called out on the fact that he is doing everything he can to avoid looking at the family home or, worse, stepping inside it. The sight is like watching the world through the lens of an apocalypse. It is recognisable, but empty, lifeless, *wrong*. Besides, watching the boxes being carted out in the arms of strangers is bad enough.

Terence can see that Julie has packed everything up with the determined organisation of a soldier. She has taped the boxes shut, like a jailer gagging the mouth of a prisoner. She has heaved all of Terence's share of the furniture into the small box room that was once his office. Each piece has a yellow sticky-note on it, so in theory, there can be no confusion for the delivery company.

Even so, Terence is asked about a desk. The removal guy wants to know if it is coming in the van or staying behind. They are all very matter-of-fact on the subject, showing none of Terence's middle-class awkwardness, nor indulging in the tactless stares of Mrs. Next Door. They all know what is going on. They have been to hundreds of these situations, the clean-up of broken homes, and they will go to hundreds more. Terence makes a mental note to give them a five-star review online.

Terence swallows. It is a simple question. *Is this desk yours?*

He doesn't know. He has no idea.

The roof of his mouth tingles; burnt and tasting of his breakfast, which has left an overly salty, dry feeling on his tongue. Terence grapples for an answer and the removal guy, for the first time, allows a faint glimmer of sympathy to grace his gaze.

Terence's lips twist. He wipes his hands on his trousers, which are creased and have a mustard stain on the left thigh.

If he takes the desk, where will he put it? What purpose will it have? It used to be where the kids' Christmas presents were stored, but he really remembers it as the desk Elle would clamber onto to grab the toys she was still too small to reach. Julie would scold him for letting her do something so dangerous, and for not storing the toys in a more suitable place. What can the desk be now? Can it have a new purpose? Is Julie even expecting him to take it, or did she leave it as a mistake? Perhaps it was too heavy for her to move.

Automatically, Terence is about to ask her when he remembers that contact between them now comes in the shape of emails and lawyers.

Terence scolds himself. He is overthinking, a dangerous game today. With no desire to fall apart in front of the removal guy, Terence decides to leave the desk and be done with it, whatever Julie wanted.

When the removal guys have unloaded and left, Terence finds himself standing in a room that is a whole house in one. It is a bedroom and a kitchen, a living room and a study, all packed into a space smaller than his garage. His old garage. Julie's garage.

Terence does not know what he was expecting, but it is a shadow of the world he's come from, the one he's lost. The boxes are piled everywhere, standing like the possessions of a stranger.

He found the room online. It looked decent in the photos, but now Terence can see it is dingy, with peeling wallpaper that reveals bare and cracked walls. There is the faint, threatening smell of mould. He soon learns that the fridge emits a sad yellow light, and the freezer does not work.

Only now can Terence count it all up. The house, dog, china, car, and kids. The other halves that fit the jigsaw of his life. Half the furniture. Half the bedding sets and half the towels. Time. Half the time with the kids. He has left behind a lot more than he has lost, because it won't fit in this room. Like the desk, and the moments he would watch his little girl climb onto it and beam with pride that she managed it.

This is not how Saturdays are supposed to go, but now Terence realises he is more afraid of Sunday. He used to know how they went too, playdates, DIY projects, and a fabulous Sunday roast. Now, the day will be an empty expanse of time. Terence has been called useless a lot recently, but only now, faced with such a Sunday, does he truly feel it.

He needs to move the boxes to create some sort of physical space that will allow him to begin unpacking, but the thought makes him feel so nauseous that he sits on the bed and tries not to look at the walls, stained by he-dreads-to-think-what.

Through a grey window, pale sunlight invades. He will have to buy curtains. He used to have yellow ones in his bedroom, a delightful splash of colour he never appreciated until now. That room had a carpet stained with family life. Crayons and coffee. That is what home smelt like. This room has only damp and dust to dance in.

He listens to the dull silence, broken only by the murmurs of his neighbours; above, below, left, right. He wonders why they have to be here. No-one is here by choice.

He misses those yellow curtains. He doesn't even know where to buy curtains; his mum bought them, then at university they were provided. After that, it wasn't his job.

Terence puts his head in his hands.

Books, he tells himself. He will force this day into various shapes until it resembles productivity, and books will be his tool. For the rest of Saturday, he will unpack and organise his books, and Sunday he will spend catching up on all the reading he didn't have time to tackle before. He will not be useless. He will not allow it.

Come Saturday night – or is it Sunday morning? – Terence finds he does not need distracting to avoid thinking. He has managed to put bookshelves up.

It is a small act that has left him dusty and sweaty, but the sight encourages him to rip open box after box, all labelled 'books,' and he works until the shelves are full.

Back home, he had had proper, custom-built cabinets that stood as tall as skyscrapers, lining the wall like his silent, watchful army waiting for orders. The books themselves were behind glass doors, as though portals in an impossible museum, protected like art, secure as children. He used to keep his own kids away, bat them back. Keep the books safe from their mucky fingers.

When they come to visit, Terence decides he will encourage them near the books. Looking at the shelves has made him realise that though this room should belong to some young thing just starting out in life, and not a middle-aged man who has lost half of everything, his life does not have be over.

The sight of his belongings slowly invading the room gives Terence strength. He will piece his life back together, and even when he builds a picture different to what he once had, it will be his, and if he changes too, it might even be better.

Home: Scenes Of A Scottish Nature

Izi Dewhurst

*There's a wonderful kind of calm the coastal air forces upon you.
Like when you finally take that deepest breath that you've been fighting
for, and at last feel your lungs stretch and fill. It's fresh, and cathartic.*

*You let the wind push past you and the waves roll in their
imperfect cadences. The sea just keeps on going. One rolling
swell after another, constant. Consistent.*

*It's clean. The air, the sand, the sea. Clean and simple.
Breathe it in deep.*

* * *

I arrived at our empty house, suitcase in tow. The upstairs windows glowed gently, but the hallway was unlit. Unlit and uncluttered. Un-lived-in.

The case got parked neatly at the foot of the stairs, delicately, so as not to interrupt the stillness. The open door revealed the expanse of my brother's room, stripped of his posters, his scattered clothes. Of his mess and of him. The piano had migrated to the other wall, beside the dismantled beams of his loft bed. A lone bookcase stood filled to the brim, like a relic in time.

A rocking chair had found its way into the room. Placed just in the suggestion of the corner, to seemingly fill up more space. To make the white walls feel less lonely. This is a perfect child's room, it said, so homely.

I'd never seen that chair before in my life.

Upstairs, the living room was ensconced in warmth, a familiar retreat from the outside world. The yellow lamp-light seeped along the staircases and under the curtains, reaching out and over the balcony above the front door. As though the house had welcomed me home, in place of anyone else.

In the kitchen, fresh paint and spritzed, wiped, and cleared sides. There was no dining table.

Instead, a pair of old armchairs had been situated in front of the bookcase, a picture of sophistication with your morning coffee. A warming and lovely scene, but they didn't live there.

The cat was curled on the Poäng. In her old age, and likely her solitude, she'd become more affectionate. She seemed as glad to see my familiar face as I was to see hers. The armchairs are in an acceptable arrangement for her, at least. Closer to her food. Did she think she was being left behind while her home faded away around her? The blank floor tiles felt less foreign as I knelt in for a cuddle.

The bookcases of recipe books, fancy tea pots, and judged-to-be-displayable crap loomed over the room, and over me. With nobody to cook for, I wondered why they were allowed to stay there. Because they looked nice.

It was our things, arranged for other people. Our home made ready for someone else. Our lives, moved along, refitted, and replaced.

* * *

I park myself in the sand of West Beach, hoping that the grains
won't find their way into my shoes. I'm woefully unprepared,
no swimwear, no sandals, no nothing, but it's too nice to stay away.
It's still a novelty to me, who has been landlocked all my life.
I've sailed in the distant past, but always inevitably returned to land.

I wonder what it might have been like to have this freedom.
To sit on the edge of the world and dip your toes into what lies beyond,
become acquainted with the water and its enormity.
It doesn't seem like it could ever end, looking over the sea now.
Just that, just sitting and looking, feels invigorating.
Like you could get lost in the same spot.

The sun shines, the wind tumbles along the coast.
Breathe it in deep. Enjoy it while you can.

* * *

We arrive exhilarated and exhausted after the nine-hour drive. On the lookout for the house, we come upon it suddenly. Swerve in. Jolt to a stop. This is it, their new home. Rented, of course, but their new home nonetheless.

We pile out of the car, into a light mist and a bracing breeze. It was welcome, really, refreshing. Now, off to the pub to collect the keys. That could have some benefits, Mum noted, having the same landlord as the pub.

Half a Guinness later, we were back.

We don't have much to unpack, with most of their belongings coming up with Dad in the moving van. All of it could wait though, as far as we four are concerned, until after we'd examined the new place and satiated our curiosity.

The pictures from the estate agent had shown a dated property, homely, but nothing special. The kind of home that had been inhabited by the same family since the sixties or so, maybe even earlier, and was lovingly taken care of even after the children were grown. Perhaps the parents had looked forward to redecorating along with a new decade, or new millennium, and put a fresh stamp on their empty nest. But they didn't have so many visitors then. Without their children's friends, or with new, unfamiliar neighbours who had their own busy lives to attend to. It would have become tiring, being there alone. And it would have rubbed off on the house itself.

All my imaginings of this slightly sad picture were shattered once we entered.

And once I saw that god-awful pink carpet.

It had been in the pictures from the estate agent, but I could only assume there had been some lighting issue that had mitigated the offence it might cause the viewer. No lovely old couple could have ever chosen this abomination. Previous tenants with questionable taste must be responsible. The curtains and lampshade were paired to it, and the ceiling accosted by a throng of adhesive glow-in-the-dark stars. This had been a child's room.

This was to be my room. The spare room.

* * *

When the tide is out on East Beach, the sands stretch further than a Vettriano landscape. I'm waiting for the dancers to appear, like in the faded little print we have at home. It feels impossible that I can leave footprints on a land that won't exist in a few hours. I wonder how people ever get used to existing somewhere so liminal, yet so decisive and unyielding.

The sea doesn't care about our plans, or our daily routines. It has its own concerns, and those won't change for anyone.

A square house stands on the hill overlooking the beach, with faded yellow walls and what must be high vaulted ceilings. It's as though it's a guardian of this part of the sea, or a beacon along the coastal path that connects the little towns. Perhaps that's where the Vettriano ladies venture down from to play their card games, and have the servants ferry the tables and parasols out.

I wonder if the Vettriano print will be coming up to the house here at all, or whether it will stay at home on its own.

* * *

Here, the mountains and hilltops are more than just rugged. 'Rugged' simply isn't enough in the face of these Olympians. They've been chipped away at for centuries, haphazardly and mercilessly, until the sheer strength of their core forbids it any longer. They make you feel like it's all a part of something much bigger than itself. 'It' of course being humanity, the roads, the few and far between settlements, the land - as though the land is so much more vast than any small mortal being could ever comprehend, never mind find the true value in, or put to its proper use.

This land will make you feel small and insignificant, yet you will be grateful for it. Hopeful.

Even in the jaws of biting cold, nothing here is fading away into grey and ash for the winter. Instead, your journey on the lone road will be chaperoned by the deep greens of fir trees, the rich brown of heather and twiggy, leafless branches, teasing you with warm terracotta and burgundy when they're banded together.

Nothing here is fading into grey and ash for the winter. The land is too stubborn to submit. It's robust, thick with life.

Black, mottled summits cut into the sky along the way, sending your path veering slowly around them, out of their shadow, and onwards deeper into what is decidedly their territory. A snow drenched cycle path runs parallel to you, and beyond that a glacier-like stream. Then, beyond some more, whether looming over you or standing sentinel in the distance, are those great and mighty hills.

Once you've reached home at last, and kept your toes free of frostbite, you'll have a warm welcome. Like the hearth has been lit especially for you, and the gentle flames wrap themselves around you, engulf you, and claim you as their own.

Of course, there is no wood-burning stove or open fire really, but Mum hugs you and squeezes you and doesn't let go. The kettle's on, wine has been opened, and there's food on the table.

Home at last.

A Seed in Soil

Emily Jayne

This was where I began. The darkness around me was damp. It crumbled at my touch, but there was nowhere for the grains to fall. For so long I remained curled into myself, waiting to be swallowed. I could feel myself stiffening, the urge to release myself from this shell became overwhelming. I stretched upwards, hoping to find an edge, or ending, to this weight. I wondered why I had not been crushed beneath the rubble of this nothing. As I crawled towards an *up*, I could not carry myself there completely. I left behind a casing and a single tether that would tie me to it. Patiently, I gained millimetres of distance. Breaking through each wave of darkness with the tip of my crown. I grew, alongside the burrowing Worms, until I pierced the surface, into something strange.

I remained rooted to the earth that had birthed me. I was unable to escape it in my entirety. What I could drag through the veil, lived in this world of weightlessness. There was only a dullness that surrounded me, the cousin of darkness, softened by space and clarity. I felt it swirl; when I pressed up against it there seemed to be no end of spaces for the spirits to collapse into. And they weren't just reactive, they moved out of glee, no thoughts wasted on necessity. They tried to carry me away with them, along with crumpled leaves and disoriented Flies. Their path wove though the trunks that towered above me.

I watched on, in awe, as the air danced. Then I was distracted by the movement sparked in the branches overhead. For a moment I was struck by warmth. It peeped though a keyhole in the canopy. It pierced through my stem and excited my cells with intention. *Grow.* It called me further into the vastness of the sky. But there was no place for me, too many giants already lavished in the pools of this golden life. So I waited and watched as the world passed in slow motion, always growing. With every breath I took, my stomach expanded. Through the seasons I grew to be resilient, protected against their unforgiving tempers. Bark fortified my figure. The part of me, I thought I had abandoned, grew also, exploring the soil beneath me. A network of my past which would remain steadfast, so I could hold my ground.

I unsheathed branches from my shoulders and danced through the stages of port-de-bras. My leaves fluttered like fans; I was finally dancing with the breeze. Its embrace could no longer subdue me. Yet what I truly craved was the Sun. It was a prize, kept from me. I was forced to be contented by glimpses only. Sunlight was my motivation and once the taste of it had touched my lips I could never have enough.

Suddenly the ground rumbled, the air, that was once so pure became a musty fog. I was engulfed by the cloud. I hid behind my shield of leaves as around me the metallic jaws of monsters chewed and gnashed and slaughtered the unarmed giants. They were even peaceful as they fell. No screams, only sighs. Their final breaths were as graceful as their lives. Accepting of their fate. I slumped, quivering, trying to accept that I would inevitably follow the woodland to the ground. But the monsters never turned on me. I was spared. I was sentenced to watch as blossoms settled with the dust, falling like bullet shells. I saw giants reduced to stumps. They littered the ground as far as the air could run. Something came and stole them in the night. Then it was only the mud and I that remained.

I was the sole recipient of the Sun's praise. Her stare bore down, weighty, more so than the soil had been when I was just a seed. It was this steel brightness that crushed me. All alone, it could so easily consume me. I had to draw my strength from below me, build to the balance that would nourish me. Light and darkness together sustained me. As I drew my strength from it, the ground began to heal. But no seedlings sprouted. Only grass, freckled by the intermittent daisies and buttercups that marked the woodland's grave. I kept growing, alone, ashamed. I sat back on my trunk and sank into myself. I hid myself from the emptiness and reached towards the sky and stars.

Then one day, strange, mobile seedlings came. Their laughter filled the air as they played. The Sun that had fed me, grown me, rooted me, seemed to be the source of their energy too. They danced and trampled over the ground, unaware of what this place had been. They plucked the daisies to make chains and crowns, like tyrants of nature. They held buttercups up to illuminate their grins. And all the while they laughed. Joy oozed from them.

I began to recognise their faces, the children, as they returned to clamber through my branches. They disturbed the Blackbirds that trilled from their perches. The children swung as the Sparrows sang. They buried their faces in my bark; I heard them whispering into me their poorly timed counts to ten. All of them bursting with excitement, squealing as friends scrambled to nests that would never be as well-hidden as the Magpie's lofty spot. Families came to collect my seeds; they took them home in plastic carrier bags. Some were tied to strings and thrown into competition. Destructive, harmless fun. No survivors ever made it deep enough into the ground. That left me alone.

Then I remembered the Worms. They're still with me, in the soil, around my roots. And in summer the insects play me a cacophony. Aside from the birds who sing me to sleep there are Squirrels who are always neighbourly. Even the children are a part of my new-found-family. So I'll whisper to them this story; the one that can only be found inside of me.

And I'll keep growing towards the sky.

Elpis, Spes and the Bottle

Sophie Kilmartin

31ˢᵗ July 2020

Spes and Elpis walk along the beach as grains of sand become embedded between and beneath their naked toes. The lowering sun touches their skin and the slight breeze nips at their hair. They turn to witness the waves soar so high, like they're flying in mid-air. Then they clash vigorously against the shore.

Soon the sky grows thicker and the stars fail to give the sisters sight, leaving only the moonlight to light a pathway against the sand. Spes steps towards the sea and allows the cold, choppy waves to crash over her feet before they drain away. If she were to walk closer, the waves would knock her over and sweep her under. She can swim, but the cold night sea would seize her body, leaving her defenceless. However, Spes thought she would like to disappear under the waves, wishing they would wash away the tears that wouldn't stop falling and blurring her vision. She could create her own sea with the number of tears she'd cried over the past 24 hours.

"Imagine what would happen if the ocean would take me. Would I entail exciting adventures, as I journey through the ocean? Or simply just drown?" says Spes.

Elpis joins her sister when she discovers a glass bottle embedded within the sand. Strange, the glass bottle was empty! No genie inside. No message in the bottle. The glass bottle was also corkless, so why was it not filled with seawater? This causes their minds to float from the beach towards a memory of a poem their nanna always told them.

The sisters sit beside the fire, with the flickering flames heating their cold cheeks. Beside the fire is a shelf. On the shelf was a DVD of *Stars Wars* (Episode IV), books of poetry by Emily Dickinson, John Keats and Emily Brontë, Alexander Pope's *Essay on Man* and *Works and Days* by Hesiod. Their nanna sits in her comfy chair and although breathless she once again told the poem.

> *In a world of greed, envy, hatred, pain, disease,*
> *hunger, poverty, war, and death.*
> *It is a timely reminder that even during our most*
> *challenging moments, there's a silver lining.*
> *The desire for a particular thing to happen.*
> *It is the thing with feathers that perches in the soul,*
> *and sings the tune without the words and never stops at all.*
> *Springs eternal in the human breast,*
> *Man never is, but always to be blest.*
> *It is the belief that allows good to triumph over evil.*
> *The only thing that remained in the jar.*
> *The only good god remaining among mankind.*
> *The great Realisation that created a fairer and kinder world.*

Elpis and Spes never understood the poem or why their nanna told them it. Nevertheless, they appreciated their time together. By the time they decided to ask their nanna, the embers from the fire had burnt out, leaving the room cold. However, the room wasn't the only thing that was cold.

"Nanna," says Spes. But she was met with no answer from the older lady who still sat in the comfy chair.

31st July 2020

Suddenly, Spes and Elpis hear familiar music that seems to be coming from the glass bottle. Turning towards the bottle they try to listen to the cornucopia tune. The music becomes so deafening that they try to block out the high-pitched noise by covering their ears before the sky flashes and the glass bottle *SHATTERS!*

1st August 2020

Daring themselves to look back at the glass bottle, they are surprised to see there is no glass bottle anymore. Instead, what was once the glass bottle now blows petals that whirl around then fall on the sand. Suddenly, the midnight air was changing into sunrise.

Elpis admires the sunrise that highlights the golden tinged sand that appears as the waves drain away. Meanwhile, the squawking seagulls surround the beach, ready for tourists to arrive to steal their breakfast. For a moment, she forgets her troubles and begins to pick up small seashells like when she was younger. Meanwhile, Spes watches the waves as they dance on the sea before the tide takes them further out.

Smiles etch onto the sisters' faces, as they realise what truly was in the glass bottle and the poem. A reminder that even during our most challenging moments, there is always hope.

Arcadia

Joseph Lee

I

Unspoiled were the meadows of Arcadia.

Even the Conqueror could see it, prowling the Steppes of this untempered land.

It had survived all the fire and blood, the slaughter and the pestilence. He had done so much to this alien plane—tugged up all life by its roots, felled every tree at the base of its trunk—and yet, it stood: bright and beautiful, sun-saturated.

It gave birth to fury in his gut.

He despised its beauty; he despised the joy of this faceless, natural splendour; how it marvelled at itself. No matter how much blood was spilled, buds of spring grew anew.

When his Master had bade him go to this place, had willed for him to smite every sinew of this living dirt, he had thought it would come with ease. Grinning would he ablate the skin of the earth, with mirth would he laugh as he watched it burn.

Yet here, now, he was so far from that thought.

He had endeavoured endlessly against the Life of this place. He had culled its herds a thousandfold, had reduced the silver-leaved trees to ash, and the rolling hills to glass.

But it was not enough.

The herds returned, younger and brighter; trees sprouted newly from the cinders of their old bodies, and the water meadows flowed anew, pooling and churning through the charred valleys of dead glass.

The Conqueror would not abide it. He, Eater of Worlds, would not be bested by these fanciful dewdrops; would not be cowed by the pleasant warmth of these pastoral winds.

He would kill it; he would snag the Life of this place by its stem, and crush it in his palm.

He would bend it to his will, no matter the cost.

He had to.

2

His slender, winged servants swarmed across the sky, thrumming over the pasture, drowning out the pleasant silence with their shrill cacophony. Their membranous wings wrought maelstroms in the firmament; tore the blue above into a bruised expanse of red and purple and black.

Great plasma-furnaces he set suspended above: they bellowed out their putrid bile, their bright-hot sickness, to drown that beautiful Arcadia beneath it.

Vaporised were the water meadows; turned to whittled beacons of malice were the silver-leaved trees, ensnared to his Master's will were the once-bright herds.

The Conqueror was gladdened; enthralled to the darkness he spread.

But it was not enough. He felt it. No matter how he choked the earth, no matter the dense breadth of his fumigation, he felt the light endure, hidden beneath the world's melting skin.

He invoked communion with his Master; sought His counsel; a means to cast utter darkness over Arcadia, that indomitable land.

Before the Obelisk, he bowed to his LORD, whose stern and stony countenance appeared in dripping plasma.

'My LORD,' the Conqueror bowed, coming to his knees before the blistering face of his Master.

'Speak,' the god demanded.

'I beseech you, SUBLIME ONE, to bestow unto me your power; enough to tear the Light from this world.'

'Thy own power is *deficient?* It is *lacking?*' the countenance dripped.

The Conqueror bowed his head. 'Arcadia's breadth cannot be culled. It burns and bleeds, and yet returns. There is yet Light within it that makes it so; while that Light remains, no end will be brought to this bountiful pasture; it shall remain unspoiled.'

The magmatic eyes of his Master boiled. 'The roots of this

World run vast and ardent. Bury deeper. Find the Tree.'

'By your will, it shall be done.'

'Go, now,' bellowed his foul majesty, 'tear it by its bark. Let nothing stand in the heart of Arcadia.'

3

And so, the Conqueror delved.

His plasma-furnaces burned with the passion of a thousand Suns, and bled so deeply into the skin of the world that nothing could see the bottom of that tarnished pit.

His membranous, chitin-servants flocked into the abscess, scuttled and chittered, and made their hives in the walls of the earth.

Their general, the Conqueror, descended into it. The furnaces had bled all that they could, and so he went into the abyss.

All was dark at first, before, alone, he came across a blinding light. He cast his putrid palm up in front of his eyes, yet it still bled through the gaps of his fingers.

He moved on, enduring, until the light became amenable.

It was there that he saw it.

It was the Tree—the Arcadian Yggdrasil—that spiralled up in countless branches of thick, white bark; its tendrils seeded through the very bedrock of the world itself.

Towards it, the Conqueror's path was clear.

He would snuff it, now; this beautiful thing. He had found the heart of Life, and would sever its aortal being.

He raised his mighty axe above his head, its shimmering edge bleeding with the plasma of his war-machines, and drew the first smiting hack into its untarnished trunk.

Another and another, the Conqueror smote the Tree, until he realised that, upon its skin, no blemish had been made.

The Tree still shone—bright and pure—and bestowed Life and Love upon him as it would any of its children.

The Conqueror seethed. He hated the Tree, despised that it cared so little for his bloody siege; that it yet stood within the centre of the earth, and was unscathed.

'What are you?' the bloodied mouth of the Conqueror spat.

From no place, and yet all places, a voice spoke back to him: *I am Life*, it said. *Who are you?*

'I am *Death*,' the Conqueror snapped.

No, the voice lilted. *You are lost.*

The Conqueror closed his mind to the voice, and brought down his axe with all his might, until all of it was spent.

Why do you do this? the voice asked.

'It is my Master's will,' breathed the broken Conqueror. 'The Universe belongs to Him, and if He is to grasp existence itself, He must become Death.'

No, spoke the soft voice. *None may become Death.* You *are all my children: you and your Master both.*

The Conqueror felt the wind against him; felt cold, here, in the pit of the world. 'Then why do we seek to kill you? Why do we burn your meadows, fell your trees, and enslave your children?'

Because you are lost, it said. *But do not fear, child... for I have found you.*

The Conqueror felt his body drift. He felt the heft of his purpose become weightless from his shoulders.

He sank towards the Tree. 'I am tired,' he said.

I know, spoke the Tree.

And there, in the birch-white nook of the Tree's roots, the Conqueror laid to rest, lost to his infernal purpose, returning, at last, to that rhapsodic sleep of eternal Life.

The Unknown of the Mind

A.B. Maloney

The unknown of the mind; the challenge of fighting an unseen illness. People do not always believe that someone is sick, but illnesses do not always have to be seen. In Freya's case, she has an invisible illness. Something which she will always struggle with behind closed doors. One day, her younger sister breaks down to their father, admitting she has not been eating what she needs to, in order to sustain her body and daily walking she has forced herself into. Freya, being away from home studying, has felt trapped, unable to help even though she would like to. Knowing exactly what her sister is going through makes her feel worse, isolated, and guilty.

She feels like she is drowning. Although everyone around her seems to be breathing just fine. Freya knows this is just her deep unconscious anxieties coming into play, like most days. For years she has been able to overcome the feeling, sometimes with help, almost as if she is pushing through the mental barrier. This is all too real to her; with what is happening to her sister. She is so unsure about the process that the team of doctors are putting her sister through, knowing that she is just as strong to do it on her own. Maybe Freya is wrong.

Someone she aspired to be like when she was in her darkest periods of life, even though she is younger Freya looks to Amie. So dark that she could barely leave her room, barely eat, and the darkest thoughts would be there almost constantly. Maybe some people need to have the professional help to get through things going on in their mind. She must trust that it is right for her sister. She knows everyone is different, but she can tell the strength within her sister.

"How did I get myself in this position? How did I let myself begin to slip this much?"

Freya looks into the mirror in her bedroom, black underneath her faded blue eyes, knowing she is not alone anymore. She has amazing people surrounding her: her family, boyfriend, and friends. Freya knows she must stay strong, be resilient and get through this to show her sister it does get better. The light will eventually shine through. Life does not always stay so dark. The road may seem like it is crumbling at each step Freya and her sister take in their recovery, but there will always be someone at the end of it for both, someone who can lend them a helping hand when the bumps or gaps in the road become too big to overcome alone.

"Freya, we're going to visit Amie. Are you coming?"

Freya jumps at the mention of her sister and quickly gets everything she might need (her mask, shoes, and coat) to then make her way to the car. The world is currently fighting off a pandemic, meaning you must wear a mask everywhere. It means visiting Amie is slightly different to normal: they cannot just go sit in her room on the ward, they must sit in a cold white marquee outside, keeping a two-meter distance.

Not even allowed to give her sister something as simple as a hug until it is safe enough to do so. A hug! The unknown of the world has thrown everything into uproar. No one knows what is going to happen, no one understands the seriousness of the mental health struggle everyone is going through to survive the day-to-day lifestyle changes.

"Will she be okay dad? I just hate seeing her so sad and distant…"

"Frey, she will get through this. She *has* to."

"It's not that she *has* to dad. You should know that by now. It's that she has to *want* to get better. That's a challenge within itself." Freya knows her dad does not quite understand mental health, but she is going to try to help him understand.

Freya plans on making it her mission to help her sister to not feel the pressure, of everything from her parents. Especially after how their Mother reacted when she found out about Freya struggling. She did not help, in any way whatsoever. Not exactly the 'Motherly' thing to do, but Freya just got through it, she had to. She will not let Amie go through it alone and she will not let her have the struggle that she had. She wanted to make sure Amie knew that there are people there for her, despite the feeling of hopelessness that Freya felt.

Freya would soon feel as if the world could collide in on her when her sister admits she does not remember some things she should, like their Christmas. The nurses explained to Freya and her father that this is what happens when someone does not eat enough, their body begins to go on autopilot, and they do not actually take in what is happening around them. But slowly, with recovery, she will begin to do things for herself and Amie will remember everything she is doing. The lost time will be made up with better and happier memories. Freya promised herself she will not leave her sister alone again.

Freya had protected Amie before she moved away. She thought that she would be okay, unaware that her sister needed strength to keep moving forward and that came from Freya. Being home, Freya will be able to look after her enough to make sure she never feels this alone again.

You need to be resilient to overcome mental health. Freya knew this and found her source of strength, even though the road was extremely challenging. Sometimes it takes a long time to get back on your feet. And sometimes it takes even longer on your own to get back to yourself again. Back to a 'Normal'.

Don't Look

Elizabeth Percy

She told me not to look.

The door was splintered and cracked, though the hole had stopped smouldering. Our bedroom door was made from a different wood to the rest of the cabin, it was lighter and a more caramel kind of brown. Mammy said that when it was built, they forgot the doors and had to use whatever they had. Daddy said that was why it had a lock on the outside. The wood around the hole was darker, I wasn't to go near it or I'd get splinters in my feet. We had to sleep in a different room for now.

El said she never liked that room to begin with. She didn't like the lock on the door. She liked to run up hills and twirl her arms around in the wind. She would climb over the tops of old boulders and jump from bank to bank over streams. When the door got locked, she'd pad over to my bed and get in next to me; just like I did to her when I was small. I didn't mind. It sometimes got cold. If the door was locked for a long while, El would venture out from the covers to look out of our window but never for long. She said she would look all day if her toes didn't feel like they would fall off. I didn't like it when she said that. All I could imagine were her toes jumping off her feet and wiggling around on the floor like fat little worms. It made me feel sick. When I'm sick and we're still in our room, El would cup her hands over my tummy and tell me she's giving me her happy. She would push her arms out rigid, hands hovering just above me so I could feel their heat, and say she was putting all her effort into making me feel better. Sometimes it worked.

We usually were let out after Daddy felt better. That's why we moved to the little cabin, for some peace and quiet. If we were noisy or if he had a bad day, we had to stay in our room. In winter, his bad days lasted longer and longer. Sometimes he told us we were noisy when we weren't. One time I had a cold and when I breathed it made a noise. I couldn't help it. We were doing a puzzle on the floor and Daddy just leapt up from his chair. His face was all purple and blotchy. As he came towards us, El took my hand and pulled me into our room. She shut the door, stepped back and watched the handle. Her fists were all balled up. We heard the door lock and then she turned around to hug me. I don't know how I could have breathed quieter and I told her I was sorry. She told me I didn't need to be.

They always went out together. Daddy would drive and Mammy would list. But Daddy hurt his foot out hunting and had to stay home for a while. When Mammy left she said she'd be super quick. Back in a flash. Two shakes of a rabbit's tail. El nodded but looked queasy. I offered to give her some happy but she shhhed me, said we were going for a nap. We were too old for naps but I went along with it anyway.

I couldn't sleep though. I laid there for so long and tried. But I was so bored. And I needed a wee. El told me we both needed a long nap and I shouldn't leave. But I really had to go. I walked as softly as I could so as not to wake her. The door wasn't locked. It opened and I walked along the corridor to the bathroom and did my business. When I came out, Daddy was stood by our bedroom door. His eyes were bleary and his cheeks were flushed. He asked me what I was doing so I told him. El appeared at the door, standing still but looking between us with just her eyes. Daddy started raising his voice, talking about peace and order and aimlessly wandering around.

He took a step towards me and instantly El did the same. He turned and moved towards her instead, she grabbed his hands and pulled him back and towards our room. He stumbled and fell, looking surprised as he tumbled across the door's threshold. I ran forwards and, as he scrambled up to try to stand, El pushed our door shut and locked it. The door shook. It creaked and vibrated and wiggled against its hinges. El looked at me, eyes wide and frenzied. She ran to the kitchen counter and pulled out the cutlery drawer, picking up knives and then discarding them. I asked her, what should we do? Daddy was angry now but we couldn't go in our room. This hadn't happened before. Maybe we should go outside, since Daddy liked to go into the woods when he was upset. She looked around wildly as if she had had an idea. I couldn't think anymore, Daddy was still shouting. El ran across the cabin to the cupboard we weren't allowed into. I wanted to follow her but I didn't want to go near our door. It looked like it would burst open at any moment. I crouched by the counter and watched as she rummaged around and pulled something out.

Daddy's gun.

It looked heavy in her hands as she brought it with great effort over to me. She gingerly placed it on the floor. El opened one of the kitchen counter doors and started pushing all the tins to the back. She took my hand and gently pushed me in it. She said I couldn't get out till she told me to. She was shaking, glancing over her shoulder and across the benches at our door. I just wanted to stay with her. I asked if she was going to lock me in. She told me she'd never lock me in, but I needed to hide for a bit, till she came back. I nodded, my eyes wettening from the idea of separation. She shut the door.

All I could hear was banging and shouting. I hugged my knees and set my shoulders against the wall. The jars and tins crowded me and I felt woozy. I heard our door groan against weight and I held my breath. I didn't know what would happen when Daddy got out. That was probably why El hid me. There was a loud booming, shattering noise. The air felt like it went white and black at the same time. My ears hurt. I didn't know what was going on but I wasn't allowed out. Where was El? What happened? I cried as quietly as I could, trying not to gasp as I sobbed.

I stayed like that for what felt like a long time. Shaking a little, I decided I needed to see where El was. Just as I had reached out to push the door, it swung open. El pulled me out and held me. She was sobbing and her whole body was shaking. I cried too but I was just happy she came back. She told me we were going to sit in our parent's room but, as I passed our bedroom, I had to promise not to look at it. I snuck a glance as we walked but I just saw the hole. El said we needed to wait in there till Mammy came home. This room was warmer than ours and there was no lock. It was nice. We cuddled as we waited; we both even got to have our naps. The cabin was peaceful now.

Send in the Clowns

Natalie Roe

The children ran around and around in circles excitedly, losing their shoes in the mud. Most of them had shoes that didn't fit properly. They had long grown out of them, so they trod down the back and wore them like flip flops. They were useless in the sludgy tracks.

The sun shone brightly down on the camp. It was drying out some of the mud but intensifying the stench of the nearby overflowing toilets.

It was quite a nice day, Azeb thought. She at least had had breakfast. She hung back from the rest of the children, solemn and unsure of herself. She looked up and heard the distant calling of seagulls. She wondered if she stood at the ferry terminal, if she could see the White Cliffs of Dover today?

It was around here somewhere.

Azeb had arrived the day before with her family. They had been on long journeys for months, some by train and also by boat. She was hungry and scared most of the time. They were disappointed when they arrived. They were running out of money, and money was the best way to get yourself in a lorry to Dover. That night, they gathered with their new neighbours under tarpaulin-roofed huts. She pretended to sleep and eavesdropped on the men talking about jumping onto the trains at the Eurostar tunnel. You could hold on tightly and arrive that way. It was okay for the adults but harder for children, and they were not recommended to try it. She'd felt guilty that her Mum and Dad were probably strong enough to go on without her.

However, she also overheard that because they were a family, they'd get moved quickly into a shipping container instead of their leaky tarp. This made them some of the luckiest people in the camp. There were proper bunk beds there. With mattresses.

Azeb had noticed the camp was made up of lots of small neighbourhoods, all named after the countries of their residents. Her Dad settled them in the Eritrean section. Next door to them was Ethiopia. She heard it being called "The Jungle" by some of the English and French-speaking people, but her neighbours didn't like it.

"We are not animals, so this is not a jungle!"

* * *

In a tent nearby, Jenny adjusted her top hat in the cracked mirror. Its bright pink feather was drooping. She would have to try and fix it when she got home. The little handbag mirror was too tiny to see her whole face, but it was the best she could manage in her present surroundings and it fit neatly into one of her many rucksack pockets.

On her chest was pinned a large white paper plate. It served as a kind of name tag, and on it was written, "Jolly Jenny". It had been fashioned by many small hands. Several had written the letters – unevenly, she admitted. One of the J's was back-to-front so it looked like a fishhook. Some gold stars had been stuck on, and glitter explosions had been glued in various firework shaped splodges. She had thanked the children who had brought her the offering profusely and seriously, as if they were visiting emperors bringing her gifts of precious gold and jewels. She allowed them to fasten the badge with ceremony and she proudly asserted she would never take it off.

She buttoned up her striped waistcoat and added a canary yellow necktie. She grinned a practiced grin and took a sip from a cup of weak tea. The teabag had been reused many times. There was no milk, (no fridge) and no sugar, (she'd brought a small bag but had used it up days ago). She was grateful to have anything to drink at all. Her own father had needed to escape, from Idi Amin, years earlier. She made it her business to never complain, not even once.

The camp often reminded Jenny of the last day of a chaotic music festival, rivers of mud, overflowing toilets, everyone looking filthy. Only with a more relentless police presence. She'd only been here three weeks. The inhabitants for months, some years.

She was wondering if this year, 2016, was her last season. The camp was only getting bigger and she was getting despondent. The newspapers back home were becoming less and less sympathetic. Even hostile. She had no idea where these people would end up.

Jenny added the final touch to her outfit. A shiny red nose. She gave it a honk out of habit. Originally, it gave out a cheeky "Eeeeeeeeee!" noise, now after many years of squeezes, it was a low "Ooooooooooo." More like a mournful mooing of a lone cow.

Still, it was nearly showtime. The smile she had on her face was a little forced, as she opened the tent flap and called out to the children to come in.

* * *

Azeb heard the call and watched the other children race across to the big tent. She stayed still, unsure, wanting to crawl back to the tarp and hide for a while.

"Jolly-Jenny-Jolly-Jenny-Jolly-Jenny!" the children cried out.

A young girl named Yordanos grabbed Azeb's arm and pulled her forwards. Azeb had met her when they first arrived yesterday. She was taller than Azeb, older, and immediately took charge of her. Yordanos was an incredibly chatty Eritrean girl, whose father was an English teacher, and so she spoke quickly and enthusiastically to everyone she met, about her escape and the long journey. She explained how thrilled she was about her new trainers, which fitted her and were watertight. How the tarpaulin of her hut collapsed under the recent rain. How she had found a teddy bear in a recent volunteer dump.

"Jolly-Jenny, this is Azeb, she is also from Eritrea!" Yordanos announced proudly. The situation in Eritrea was not one that Jenny had been familiar with, until starting this job. She'd freely admit she had to look it up. It was barely mentioned back home.

"Good morning, Azeb!" Jolly Jenny replied.

"She's here with her Mum and Dad; she doesn't talk much. She's new."

Azeb regarded Jenny with suspicion. She didn't feel like talking. This tall English girl was dressed weird. No one else in the camp looked like this.

The show began.

Jenny handed out bright neon-coloured plastic plates for spinning and gave each child a stick to balance it on. Some children were practiced at this and immediately set to the task with great concentration. Yordanos was a natural and kept her eyes hawk-like on the spinning orange plate, tongue slightly extending for her mouth. Azeb hung back. She shook her head when Jenny came around with the plates and hunched down to watch instead.

Azeb crouched, arms folded, face creased like a care-worn old woman, not looking like a child at all. The other children giggled as the plates span off in crazy directions, one flew out of the tent and a tiny boy scampered off to get it, tripping as he went. Azeb coolly watched.

Jenny kept one eye on her. She'd seen so many like her before. She knew if she could just get her to giggle even slightly, she might turn back into a kid again. Jenny knew exactly the scenarios she would have been through. The stories were all too similar, wherever they were from across the world.

Childhood shouldn't just be about surviving till the next border, thought Jenny.

* * *

Azeb hung back throughout the morning as Jenny led a song of nonsense words.

"Flea?"

"Flea Fly!"

"Flea Fly Flow?"

Azeb stayed uninvolved and murmured a few words. Yordanos was singing merrily. She took hold of Azeb's hand and started to swing it back and forth to the music. Azeb was fascinated by the clown and her funny clothes. It reminded her of her own birthday party she'd had over a year earlier, of her Dad who had given her a bicycle and being surrounded by friends.

The song stopped and everyone gave a round of applause. Jenny clapped back at the children and gave a little bow. She looked back over to Azeb with a smile.

Slowly, carefully, Azeb unfolded herself and made her way forward until she was facing Jenny.

Jenny knelt down.

Azeb reached out her hand and honked the clown's red nose. "Ooooooooo!" it went, in its cow-like way.

Her eyes started to sparkle; then she began to smile and then to giggle and then to laugh. She did it again.

"Ooooooooo!"

Jenny raised her hands to her head to make cow horns and imitated it: "Moooooooo!"

She took the nose off and placed it on Azeb's nose.

Azeb gave it a welcoming honk, then ran away back to Yordanos who was collapsing in giggles. She couldn't wait to show it to her Dad. The rest of the children joined in, as did Jenny, heartily.

"Maybe one more tour," she thought. "It's worth it."

The Shape of Resilience

Megan Tinker

As the national lockdown drew on, the news reported more and more sightings of a 'Resilience'; almost like reanimated shadows that had grown hair and facial features, our Resilience were beings that followed us around and tried to make life a little easier for us. My Resilience, who was smaller than me with grey eyes and blonde hair, liked to organise my bookshelf in a different pattern every day. When it wasn't organising the little pieces of my life, it was trying to exercise, something that I'd avoided due to a lack of motivation and energy. It liked to do this as it followed me around the house: when I walked along the upstairs landing it did lunges. In the evening, watching the television it would flex its biceps in the mirror, humming as it did so. And when I finally went to bed, it would dance as if it were in an 80s fitness music video, like the ones with the woollen headbands and luminescent tights. When I woke up, it would sit by my bookshelf mimicking sounds such as typing on a keyboard or the sound a bow makes when an archer draws an arrow. It tapped each book individually before showing it to me.

"Yes," I said to it. "It's a book."

My friend called me to ask what my Resilience looked like.

"It sort of looks like," I paused, taking a moment to observe my Resilience as it began to organise my coats by colour, "me."

"Urgh! You are so lucky," my friend said. "Mine looks like a deformed Danny DeVito. It tried to lick my dog-hey! Don't touch that! Ugh, I've got to go."

As my friend hung up my Resilience looked over at me with a blank stare. I'd noticed, only recently, that its face had started to morph into something like mine: rounded cheeks, sunken eyes, and a set of bushy eyebrows. The grey in its eyes had started to warm to an auburn colour and its hair was changing from blonde to ginger. It had started to grow in height until we measured the same in feet and inches, and it had even developed a tiny freckle on its right cheek, just like I had. I watched as it pointed towards its open mouth.

"What?" I asked. "Are you hungry?"

It didn't reply. Instead, it made the sound of arrows gliding on a bow and lunged across the landing.

* * *

The change in my Resilience came at a time when things had started to grow sour. The lockdown had started to take a toll on me; I refused to leave my bed before late afternoon, and even then, I still struggled to sleep at night. I tried to regulate my days by sticking to a schedule: waking up at a similar time, taking my medication, eating, eating again, watching a film, and then going back to bed. But the days and the hours soon merged into one, the outside world became a treacherous land which I soon grew to fear, my notebooks and other documents had begun to pile up in an unorganised manner, and one of my plants had shrivelled up dry.

I'd been an archer long before lockdown when the idea of my Resilience was nothing more than words on a page and a burning sensation in the pit of my stomach. I'd been a Great Britain hopeful, training to become a future World Champion, but when the world shut down my bow was packed away into its box along with my motivation and I had not touched it since.

It drove my Resilience insane.

It reorganised my desk and other documents from Z to A and had organised my bookshelf by the colours of the covers. It had watered all of my plants, paid my bills, made my bed, and sent texts to all my friends.

It had now been two months. I had done nothing, and my Resilience had grown impatient. It gestured to my bow box with a blank expression.

"I don't understand," I said to it. "That's my bow. What about it?"

It frowned – something it hadn't done before – and got to its feet and began to tap on the box's hard shell. Not only did my Resilience resemble me in appearance, but it had also started to dress like me too, with its skinny jeans, oversized T-shirts, and second-hand trainers. When it walked, it did little hops on the opposite feet.

I ignored it as it tapped away without rhythm. It stared at me from across the room as it banged away on the box like an angry drummer. Its frown grew into a look of annoyance and then morphed into a hateful expression. It punched its fists against the metal frame, and soon enough, the box fell to the floor with a crash.

"Hey!" I leapt to my feet, slightly spooked. "What are you doing?"

My Resilience marched over to me and pressed its forehead against mine. It held its hands on its hips and, despite its cherry pigmentation, its cheeks burned red. Although it could not speak, I could hear the angry puffs of breath escaping its lungs.

"What? What do you want?!" I shouted at it. It said nothing, as usual, but gestured over to the box and pointed to the sticker that had my name written on it. Next to it, a picture of me from my last tournament, holding a silver medal.

"I don't understand," I said to it again. It rolled its eyes – a habit I did too – and kicked the box with the heel of its foot. When I didn't respond, it did it again. And again. And again. "Okay! Okay, okay. Stop it."

I pushed my Resilience away, its skin ice cold. I unlocked the box and removed the lid, finding my dismantled bow staring back at me. The feel of it, the cold, harsh metal felt strange to touch and the very sight of it made me nervous. All competitions had been cancelled – the Olympics especially – and so I hadn't practised, let alone picked my bow up, in months. As I admired it, all the intricate curves and the smoothness of the arrows, my Resilience tapped the box with its foot.

"You want me to shoot?" I asked it. It said nothing. Neither of us said anything for a long time.

Eventually, my Resilience took the pieces of my bow and began putting it together. I watched as it struggled to click and screw the pieces into place. Whenever I tried to add a suggestion or offer any help, it slapped my hand away and clicked its tongue, which I took as a sign to let it be.

When it had been set up properly, taking much longer than usual, my Resilience handed me my bow and arrows and pushed me outside. It was now June, so the summer sun beat down on me and I struggled to see due to its bright rays. From behind me, secure and safe inside, my Resilience watched from the window with two nosy eyes. When I didn't move, it rolled its eyes, flicked the window, and mimicked the sound of an arrow hitting a target. As I headed into the garden, still somewhat bewildered with the way my Resilience was acting, I turned to see it smiling at me from the window, its thumb stuck out an odd angle – its poor attempt at a thumbs up.

With each day that I practised, I felt a lump of hope build up inside me and the summer air refreshed my dusty, cooped-up lungs. I let myself fall into a rhythm: I was finally sleeping again, and the hours of the day dispersed back into their normal pattern. My Resilience seemed to relax too. It spent less time following me around and more time watching me shoot from the window, somewhat proud. On the days where I felt too tired to move, my Resilience kicked the bottom of my feet and clicked their fingers next to my ears, stirring the energy inside me to continue.

* * *

My Resilience did not disintegrate before me like the others I'd heard of. When things eventually returned to normal, I found my Resilience staring out of my bedroom window with a look of contentment. It looked exactly like me now, as if it were the identical twin I'd never had. As my life regulated and fell back into place, my Resilience patted the top of my head and winked, before walking out of my house and down the street, disappearing into the surroundings. The space around me seemed empty, as if my Resilience had not existed to begin with. The only thing that represented its presence in my life was a stack of books by my bed: all piled in a neat, alphabetical order.

Something Red, Purple and Lovely

Maia Tudor

3

Vodka sticks to my throat like wet paint and dries before I can glug my Diet Coke to take away the chemical taste on my tongue. "Oh my god! You look gorgeous," my mum shrieks. "Thanks mum, but please don't go telling my friends that this is one of your old dresses when they pick me up. It's embarrassing." The tides of me and my mother connect in their breaks before pulling away from our shadows in the hallway. A car beeps outside and my mum wraps her dressing gown around her tighter. "Have a good night lamb, no kissing boys and make sure you all stick together!" My legs feel clammy and big as I waddle to my friend's Toyota in 3-inch heels. My mum looks dainty and old as I wave from the passenger seat, and I miss the smell of her night cream.

The club smells of aftershave and sweat, my breasts quiver under silk and my body oozes something wet. Fat pink shapes and fast rippling spirals are projected onto the dance floor amidst short black dresses and tight white shirts. Christmas music shudders through my limbs and spits cold lyrics into my mouth. "Shots! Right girls, I'll get the first round. Should we all just have a jägerbomb for now," my friend Cara screeches. We all scream "yes," and the night begins to bend into something fizzy and wonderful.

The smoking terrace reeks of people, their alcohol breaths and breakup stories, wavering hand gestures and drunken stumbles. The cold night sways between the bare legs of strangers and seeps through the sleeves of thin jackets. I exhale and watch creamy smoke rise into twilight and fade into tiny beads of black poison. The light turns orange and dim. "Well, if it isn't my favourite writer." The gorgeous spill of her voice uproots every dozy vessel in my limbs and softens the hard shells of my goosebumps. "Lillie!

I… I thought you were doing a year abroad? Belgium?! Your last letter said that you wouldn't be home until… February? I can't believe… You look… How are you here," I ask, my heart thumping. "Well, my module got cut short and my parents kept nagging me to come back, so I got home yesterday. And I missed you." Pearl coloured powder glints from the inner corners of her eyes, her eyelashes undulate in slow motion and in the smallness of the moment, I love her.

8 months later

2

Water glides over my stomach and wades its way down my ear tunnels until the lake falls silent. My body sighs and balances on top of each slow ripple, jerking when a pebble stirs beneath me. I extend my every limb until my edges begin to unravel and bleed into the riverbed. Sunlight melts through my eyelids and beams loud red nothingness into my vision. I wake from my daydreams and begin to swim back to my friends.

Dew drops slide down my legs as I dry in the warmth, new blood tickles my cold toes and turns them thick and blotchy. The sun reflects on each dip of the lake and ruptures its surface into fantastic white light, glistening onto the ridges of the grass banks. I hunch over on my towel and open my copy of Alice in Wonderland. I form the sentences lazily before they drift far away. I burrow one of my fingers into the dirt beside me and get stung by a nettle. In pain, I look up to watch Lillie dancing in the lake.

The sky becomes peach and timeless, the hills stretch far beyond the lake and turn into trembling purple shadows. "You talk to me like I'm the only person in the world but can't even look at me when we're together. Why do you do that?", Lillie murmurs. She sits beside me on a mossy slope and looks down at the lake and sighs, her wet body twitching beneath her lilac towel.

A light breeze weaves around our bodies and leaves a beautiful stillness. The world curls up tight and exhales. I turn to look at her and do the same, "because, looking at you is like looking at the sun. It blinds me of everything else." The hardened things in the world become blunt and my words are planted deep within the wet soil beneath us – my love for her blooms around our bare ankles.

I

The little hot ball subsides, the mosaic patten of her lips press against mine and something sweet and fragile emerges from its sleep. She pulls away from me and I watch wet prisms form on top of her eyelashes, "Iris…"

Home/Office

Emily Walker

I have started screening your calls. Not with a fancy electronic system. It's just me recognising the 512 at the end of your number. You call *that* often. Even then, I still have to answer. My skin shivers, my chest tightens, every time you call. Before, in the office, your calls were safeguarded by coffee breaks and across-the-desk eye rolls. They fell into the daily rhythm of photocopying and minuting meetings. I miss the office for that.

I have saved your file onto my desktop, for easy access. The page takes a while to load as your phone number pings into the *next caller waiting* box. In these ten seconds, I notice my aching shoulders and roll them back, each bone clicking like the spokes of a bike wheel, reminding me to take a screen break. I feel reluctant to move away from my office corner, fearing your voice will stain the walls of my flat. I imagine you seeping into the bedroom, the kitchen, my cup of tea. I stop myself from imagining what you look like. You are a faceless thunder cloud, the sound of rain outside as I lie in bed. That is how I want you to stay.

Our calls typically follow a detailed itinerary of the various inconveniences our company has inflicted upon you, or how a member of our staff has committed some moral failing, that has warranted a formal complaint. They are often fabricated or exaggerated. I am not important here, but I feel personally responsible for your grievances. Every "do you know what I mean?" curdles in my stomach, producing a feeble "mmm, yes... I understand" response when you give me the opportunity to speak.

I type up every complaint and pass them to my manager, peppering my emails with "sorry to bother you" and "apologies for the inconvenience." This tedious ritual haunts my otherwise uneventful workday. My old, office view of Angelica in Accounting has been replaced by a skyline of newly built, high-rise flats and Leeds smog. I spend most of my lunch break stood on my balcony, emerging from my underwater cave into a tiny air pocket, before plunging back into the phones. You have normally left a voicemail or two when I return.

Occasionally, you go on a tangent and reveal little clues about yourself. The first time you did, it was so brief, I didn't take note of it until I spell-checked the transcript. You had been criticising a company policy when you said, "and now there's only me in the house!"

Now there's only me.

I have always assumed you lived alone, Ms. 512 (Data Protection prevents me from disclosing your name). I never hear you talk to anyone, no one chimes in from the background of your calls, which I would expect considering how often we talk. The *now* in your sentence throws me. Someone has left you, recently too, but you have never mentioned this before. I presume it is a partner of some sort, perhaps a housemate. Are you too old for a housemate? I can't guess your age. You are acidic and eroded, still full of bite. I presume you are older than me.

Did *they* leave you intentionally, whoever it was? Did someone pass away? I don't like thinking this, your roots are squirming into my mind. Increasingly, you throw in new scraps of information like, "I just want them home" and, "It wasn't my fault." I can almost see you, sat on the dining chair opposite me, behind a veil, or through an unfocused lens. Blurred. Close. Until I blink you away.

Once, you rang me in tears. You began to speak, then paused, whispered something in gibberish and finally hung up. You didn't call back for two weeks after that. I felt relief eventually seeing your 512 on my screen, mostly because I didn't have to organise a welfare check. I obviously tell my manager what we talk about, who now asks me to CC our Safeguarding Lead into any emails regarding you. Safeguarding Lead never replies to the emails, except once when they asked me to clarify whether you had said "die" or "dye." Stupid question.

You phone me today. It's raining and clammy. I am just making a cup of tea when 512 flashes up. The phones have been quiet so far and I am still in my pyjamas, my new work uniform. I open your file, click to answer your call and reel off my usual company script.

"Hello, it's Ms. 512." You pause. Wind snatches the rain and throws it so that it rattles against my window. I am sat shivering, refusing to turn my radiator on after a concerning electricity bill last month. I have noticed some black mould in the corners of the flat recently. When this happened in the office, I informed the cleaners about it, who scrubbed the mould away within the hour. In my flat, I am the office cleaner, but I don't get paid for that, so the mould will likely stay.

You are breathing heavily, each inhale labouring against you. I accidentally scratch my nail into the wooden table, driving a splinter into the nail bed. I attempt to pull it out, but I break the skin, wedging the splinter deeper into my finger. You continue to say nothing.

"Is everything okay, do you want to talk about it?" I am off script now, but you have been off script for weeks.

"I'm sorry... I know I always chew your ear off. It's just nice to have a reason to talk to someone. When the kids left, I just didn't know what else to do. I'm on my own all the time." The splinter has driven so far into my finger it has now drawn blood.

As you talk, and I bleed, I find an email from Safeguarding Lead sent earlier this morning, concerning you, asking if we have spoken today. They have CC-ed new people into our correspondence that I don't recognise. Two of them are from Social Care. One is from the police. I read through the previous emails on the chain. Every detail is marked as confidential or redacted, your date of birth, your address, your children's names. I can't help myself.

Opening a new tab, I type your name into Google. There you are, with an accompanying mugshot and a litany of newspaper articles. You're not how I expected you to look, your blurred shadow now focused into sallow eyes and wiry hair. I see you. I don't want to know what you did, or why your kids were taken away, so I close the tab without reading any of the details.

My splintered finger has left a blood stain on the dining table. I decide to terminate the call, emailing my manager to say that I no longer feel comfortable listening to you, that Safeguarding Lead should now take over, attaching your file and deleting it from my desktop. I think about the other file with your name on it, somewhere out there, featuring a chapter of my transcripts. An appendix, a footnote, to a much larger report. One I would never like to read. I will not let you flood into my home.

Box

Max Watt

It was the night of the meteor shower. I was in the new flat, unpacking. I had my hand deep in a box when I felt a sharp pain. I yelped. Yanked my hand out. Looked at it. There was nothing at first. Just the white, torn skin. Then the blood came thick and fast. It ran between my thumb and forefinger. *Bastard.* I ran to the kitchen and stuck my hand under the tap. I watched the blood swirl down the drain. I had no plasters, no bandages. Nothing like that. Just boxes. So, I kept a grip on it until the blood stopped. It took about forty-five minutes. I sat on the floor with my back to the sofa. Gripping my hand, surrounded by the boxes.

When I remembered about the meteors, I went onto the balcony. I couldn't see a thing through the light pollution. I stood there a while, staring up. A thick fog in the air. No sign of anything. It was now, in this moment, that the feeling came into full fruition. I wanted...hell, *needed* a beer. I don't know how these things happen. One minute everything's fine, the next it's too much.

I kept looking up as I went through the streets. There was nothing. Always nothing. There was a homeless guy next to the shop, his back to the wall. He woke as I went by. Inside a sleeping bag that was resting on a folded out cardboard box. His beard was short. Shorter than other hobos I've seen, anyways. And his clothes didn't look too scuffed.

I went past him into the shop and found the aisle with the alcohol. When I looked at the beers, they all blurred into one. I grabbed a crate of fifteen. The guy at the till seemed wary of me when I put them down on the counter. He had this look. It made no sense to me. It never did. So many people bought beer. Was it that obvious?

As I left, the homeless man perked up, leaned forwards and said, "Oi, mert. A couldn't grab a can off ya, could a?"

I could feel the box rubbing into the cut and breaking the skin open again. A moist feeling was developing in my palm. Usually I'd keep walking, but something about this one, about this *time*, got me. I turned, studied him. I said, "They're bottles," and tucked the crate into my bag.

"Now come on," he said. "Help a brother out."

"No."

"Now what's the fuckin problem. Ya look like a well-to-do young one. What's the issue with helpin a brother out, now?"

Under my breath, almost to myself, I muttered, "You want things I have. I don't think that's as good a thing as you think it is."

He sat up and looked me straight in the face. "What's one can, eh?"

"Nothing, when you have none. Everything when you can afford many."

"Now, to me that says *some*thin. You're a well to do one, a can tell."

"I only have a small amount of money."

"Am askin for one can. One fuckin can. What are you, a stingy cunt?"

"I'm not looking to share."

"Fuck off then, ponse. Ya dopey fuckin twat."

"You ought to calm down," I warned him.

I walked. It was no better way out here. I still couldn't see the stars. The closer I got to the flat, the more I thought about it all. Those boxes and the potential of nothingness. The unexplored nowhere. It appealed to me tonight. The trouble was, I simply had too much stuff.

I was a few streets away. I thought about cracking a bottle there and then. But no. The voice of reason was greater than the impulse. *What are you, an animal? Just wait til you're home. You got glasses, a sofa. All you gotta do is unpack the glasses...*

I stopped in my tracks. My heart beating anxiously. I went forwards, towards the flat.

Soon as I got in, I attacked the boxes. Ripped one open. Dug deep. Until I found the one. I shook it. It rattled, metallic. I weaseled my arm through and grabbed the knife. I eased it out.

Held it up. The false light glinted off it. My blood still wet on the metal. I put it in my coat. Grabbed the box. Heaved it up. Just a few times more, I told myself. And then no more.

I found him with his back to the shop. He saw me and cried out, "Ere e comes again. What? Decided one crate ain't enough for..."

I dropped the box in front of him. Its landing was somewhere between a crash and a thud. "Take it," I said.

He looked down at it. Confused. "What's in it?"

"I don't know. Just take it."

"Ya don't know? Fat lotta good that is, pal."

"It's stuff. Stuff you don't have. I don't want it. Just take it. I'll be back with more if..."

"More? Bloody ell, lad. Where am a s'posed to put it? Get this shite out of ere."

"But..."

"*Get.*"

His finger pointing. Commanding. I froze. After a time I asked him about the beers.

"What *about* em? Ya stingy self needs the ole lot, I thought."

"If I give you one, will you take the box?"

He looked confused. "You're fuckin weird, lad," he said.

"I'm serious. If I give you a can, will you take the box?"

"Fuck off."

I opened my coat and reached in and lifted the knife up so he saw. Stared him down so he knew. He squinted at me. Confused. Brick wall. He didn't even have fear. But that changed. I pulled the knife out and stuck it in. Everything ripped as I tore it across. The man went immediately quiet. Then I picked the box up and turned it upside down and tipped everything out of it. Its innards smashed on the ground. Plates. Cutlery. A toaster. A kettle. I cut the rest of the tape and folded the box down and gave it to him. "Here," I said. "Now will you take the rest? One bottle per box."

He stared at me for a moment. He was confused. Incredulous. He said. "Sure. Fine. But know this, am no charity case, ya got it, psycho? Ya better come back with the beer, or you'll need more than a knife."

"I'm not looking to be charitable," I told him. I turned off the main road and headed onto a backstreet where the streetlamps were all off. Finally, the light pollution had cleared and I could see the stars. For half a second I thought I saw a meteor. I thought I did, but I'm pretty sure I didn't. They were out there somewhere. Out there in the empty space. Where nothingness was everything. And I thought about how, if just one was directed the right way, it could turn all my stuff to dust. And I smiled.

Cat and Mouse

Indee Watson

I wake up in a bed that's not my own. The mattress is lumpy and stained under the cover, which is hanging off the end. That's stained too.

The room I'm in is small, the window smaller still. Sunlight leaks around the edge, spilling across the walls, but the window is otherwise hidden, rusty nails forced into wood and pushed further into the windowpane.

Someone doesn't want me to be seen.

When I sit up, my head swells with pressure, searing pain forcing me back into the pillow. My vision is fuzzy, my eyelid's sheer pink flesh distorting into a blur, each thud in my head summoning a flash of light that erupts across my eye's rosy sky. It's another fifteen, maybe twenty minutes before I manage to sit up again, and though my head is still banging, the pain has somewhat subsided. Without this distraction I can feel the cold, a big gap under the door letting in such a draft that my bare skin whimpers, goosebumps protruding all over my flesh. It's no wonder I'm so cold; I'm wearing very little, men's boxers and a ripped t-shirt. Neither are mine.

As I step onto the floor, tattered wood splintering my feet, my legs nearly buckle, a weakness encapsulating me. It takes a while for me to be able to stand on my own. When I can, I drag myself to the window, trying to prise off the wood, my fingernails beginning to peel away from the pink flesh of my fingers. It's to no avail. The eye is shut tight. My heart begins to beat louder than my head, a warbled breath emitting from my lips, unsteady and quick. But I don't have time to collapse, or cry, because a shuffle emerges from under the door, and my breath nearly stops entirely. It's quiet at first, the steps slow and calculated, but as they grow nearer, they grow louder, booming footsteps now echoing into the room, as though the heart of the house is beating around me. I scramble to find somewhere to hide, but the room is virtually empty and my best attempt is to crouch in the corner, legs pulled up to my chest. That's when I notice the bruises sprouting across my limbs, large purple patches shaped like handprints and accompanied by a plethora of scratches. As I look, my hair falls by my face, my vision now just a small strip of the room in front of me. But in that strip I see the door and the shadows of feet on the other side. They stop for a second, hesitation rife in the air. Though seconds later, with a rusted squeak, the handle turns and the door creaks open to show a man I don't recognise. He's much taller than me, padded out with muscles that would far overpower my own. His hair is greying, slicked to his head like scales, extending across his shoulders, and his eyes are obscured with anger. He sees the blood that has started to dribble from my fingertips.

"You think you can just pull off the wood, easy as that? You're not going anywhere. If you try, I'll do more than hit you. Now, I'm leaving for a bit. Got some…business to attend to. There'll be boxes in front of this door. If you even dare try opening it, you won't be able to put them back. I'll know, and I'll do something you *really* don't want me to do. Understand?"

With trembling lips, I nod, and his face changes for a split second. He seems almost apologetic as he glides towards me, his neck craning to look me in the eyes. His breath is stale, a smoker's breath, and his teeth are yellow.

"I really don't want to hurt you, darling. Respect me, and I'll keep you safe. Besides, they're not missing you out there. You're better off here," he hisses.

His smile is almost kind.

He grabs my face and plants his rubbery, wet lips on my own. His oscillating tongue flicks into my mouth, a stifled moan crawling up his throat before he pulls away.

"You be a good girl."

Stunned, I remain still as he turns and creeps away. The door slams shut and with some hesitance, he slides two boxes in front of the door, the weight creaking the floorboards below. And with that, he slinks out of sight.

Something starts to swell up inside me, building up like a storm. It starts so small, just a pinprick of emotion, spiralling into a whirlwind in my stomach. It's a feeling I can't quite untangle, some sick mix of fear and hatred, crawling inside my flesh. Something in me changes. I drag myself across the room, a broken nail catching my skin and tearing. My eyes instinctively well up but I force my mouth shut. The blood begins to spill from my torn flesh, leaving a pool that will most certainly stain the wood it covers. Perhaps that's not such a bad thing.

My body is charged with desperation as I kick the door. Nothing.

I kick again. Nothing.

I still haven't heard his car rev up, but I don't care. I kick again.

On the third try, the boxes begin to shuffle forwards, the light spilling in as the door opens wider. I thud my feet against it until the wood cracks and my feet turn pink. But to my surprise, it works. Before I leave the room, I glance at the ring on my middle finger. It was my gran's ring, a thin strip of woven silver, two rubies guarding a large jet heart. My gran was the *only* one with a ring like this, and now so am I. The only one to have this ring. I struggle to pull it off my fingers, my hands shaking frantically, but eventually I do and with some carelessness, it ricochets against the wall. I nudge the ring far under the bed, where he won't see it. Where nobody will see it...unless they're looking for it.

Without turning back, I bolt out of the room, barely noticing the ache in my feet as the bruises turn from pink to purple. I run, and with some false alarms along the way, reach the front door, grab the handle and...it's locked. Of course it's locked. As I scramble through drawers searching for the key, cutlery and take-out menus flying everywhere, something raps on the door and through the frosted glass, he's there.

"Looking for these?"

The clinking of keys is muffled by the door, though his voice doesn't struggle to get through. An air of panic fills the room, and I race back through the house as he fumbles with the keys. From the kitchen, glass shatters, shards bouncing off the walls and raining down on me, varnishing the wounds already rife on my skin. Like a chorus answering the shattering verse, somebody whimpers from the far end of the house, where a door sits tucked away behind an old coat rack. How many others are there? I don't have time to ponder the question, desperately searching for another way out. Before he creeps into the hall, I fold myself behind a door, my lungs full and steady as I hold my breath.

"Come back here, now. You don't wanna make me angry."

The floor shakes as he rumbles through the house but I remain hidden, my body fading into the room like a wallflower. He slithers into his den to search and I slip away, tumbling through the carcass of my abduction.

The house pants,
The walls close in with each breath
And I navigate the labyrinth,
a mouse to his cat,
the house's stomach churning me through its system.
That's until I see the sunlight,
the grass,
the sky,
the trees waiting outside.
I grab the doorhandle,
I turn the rusted metal and…
it clicks, the door swinging open.
With the autumn air on my skin,
I run
and run,
never looking back
until my legs cave
and I fall,
and I hear him shouting,
but it's too late
because someone finds me
and I'm…safe.
I'm safe.

He reaches towards the voice recorder and switches it off.

"Thank you, Hayley. After identifying the blood in his house as yours and finding your ring, we believe we have found and detained your abductor."

His smile is one of pity.

Mine is one of relief.

"Before I go, can I ask – did you find anyone else in his home?"

"We found two girls, scratched up but otherwise unharmed. He fled when you escaped but we picked him up at a local gas station."

"Thank you, officer. And my ring?"

"Will be returned to you when this is all over."

I nod, turning towards the door.

"When all this is all over," I reassure myself.

And I smile.

Meltdown

Hannah Cross

Imagine drowning on air.
    Imagine suffocating on frothing rage
        Imagine each sense feels like ice cold rain pelting
      against a tin roof

You can't see a way through
    You have been here before
        In hoarse screams of trembling fear

But it does subside
    Each and every time
        Even though it couldn't possibly

Shame is what you are left with, embarrassed at the swirling
emotion
    And the way your body goes stiff
        And the way you hurt yourself
            So that beads of blood break the skin on your
            arms
                And you shatter everything into a thou-
                sand pieces

The pacing begins
    The flapping
        And squeezing your teddy so tight
            It is a black hole, with no way through
                over
                    under
                        around.

Until there is.

A persistent sun muscles through your storm
    A tender teal sky reminds you that you always
    Always
        Fight your way through

Cloudbusting

Leah Figiel

You sit; weight sagging on the grass. In front of that marble stone,
your life, inscribed in gold.

Your voice pushes through the rain that beats my skin and flushes
my ears and you are at peace, at rest, in control.

But the wind blows the paper bags in bloom. Petals disband
and become brown, dusty and old.

Five years get stuck here,
the stubble of soil I threw on you pulls my hands again, making a
mould.

I'm sure that was you
waving at me in stop motion,
the relentless raindrops blink, behold

like camera snaps you come and go, an apparition, made of va-
pour and clouds. But I saw you once, that counts I suppose.

I return home, to find a white feather placed beside a snapshot of
us, smiling. You once existed, and *that* is my source.

Gingerbread Men

P.J. Hale

I'm a Gingerbread Man
Digested by threat and urgency
Driven to madness by survival
Welcome to The Emergency

I'll keep on running as fast as I can
Through every day and every night
No rest for any of us
My whole nation must dodge the bite

Yet the bite keeps on snapping
For 800-years and now still
You may have eaten our arms and legs
But our spirit you will not kill

Just when I think we're free
Across you roar again
If I stumble now it's all for nothing
Our run will be in vain

Unlike the Gingers that ran before me
I ponder a risky thought
What if I stop.
Face the fox – a chance to be caught

Run, run as fast as you can
You can't consume me; I'm an Irishman.

I'll find time

Poppy Halliday

It's not a bullet going straight through.
More like shrapnel
massacring,
from the interior.
Yet the poison is fucking
delicious,
enticed by the dying fruit.

Flesh as brittle as ceramic.
Fragments of
spoiled ivory china,
sitting on my blemished skin.
'Out damned spot.'
But the marks grow bigger.

Becoming polluted by anticipation
and distorted
with shame.
All while my life could be reduced to,
governed by
an acronym, four bleak letters.

They say
Don't die of ignorance
and maybe I already did.
Yet I choose to grin,
blindly so that
I may live.

Everyday Musings of Current Affairs

Lucy Morton

today is cancelled
due to lack of interest
shut the shops
                    bars
                        cafes
daysdriftingintoone
sleeves r e a c h i n g into one another
a constant loop
wanting things to change wanting things to change
   wanting things to change
needing things to change
needing is powerful
dragging the purest of souls to
the darkest of hells
corrupting the most innocent wishes with
selfish desire
even the word is dirty
C O R O N A V I R U S.
fear melts into anger
i can't
persuade into progress
you   into the unknown
     fall
crashing before your own eyes
thinking a train is moving when
sitting still. a victim
of uncertainty
– but –

while the disease *disrupts* humanity
the world thrives
without the disease *of* humanity
how can a setback of this magnitude
feel like a step   forward
in the right direction?
are you alone in this?
or are you just simply
alone

Persistence

Rachel Wainwright

Coronavirus is the biggest threat this country has faced for decades.
All over the world we are seeing the devastating impact of this invisible
*   killer.*

A worldwide operation, all because of a deadly mutation,
spreading, infecting, causing silent devastation to sweep across the
    nation,
hearing the newspaper's narration, as we watch safely from isolation,
as thousands of members of the NHS get into formation,
caring, curing, researching to provide information,
as they wake each day in the face of devastation and instead
    choose
determination.

It's vital to slow the spread of the disease.

The government advise us to stay inside as they try and plot the
    virus' demise,
as we survive, if we feel confined, we remind ourselves that we are
    saving lives,
and there are no goodbyes, only see you next time.

The time has now come for us all to do more.

Look at what you have done already.

A dedicated army veteran restoring faith in humanity,
walking laps of his garden to raise money for charity,
the public clapping, standing in solidarity, a whole community,
in a time of uncertainty, we show unity.

The patience and common sense you have shown.

We can take heart from today's news,
which has the makings of a wonderful British scientific achievement.

A vaccine created from genius, scientists' brilliance,
as we provide each other with reassurance, allowing for
  persistence,
endurance, not giving in and showing resistance, perseverance,
  resilience,
we will get through this, as we remain consistent keeping our
  distance,
in order to protect those who are dearest.

A one-way road to freedom.

We keep on going, nearly there, as we leave tragedy in the rear-view
  mirror.
A challenging year – for those we lost we say a prayer,
and think of all the memories shared. For in the future we declare,
to savour each precious moment and treat life with care.

Seasons of hope.

New seasons, new life as spring is in sight,
bringing better days, brighter days.
Seemingly endless with warm nights, festivals with flashing lights,
beer gardens and friends who cheers with their pints.
As the sun sets, despite it all,
there is life.

Delirious Mutterings of a Time in Limbo

Jess Wright

We tiptoe,
through milky silence,
sundrenched and sleepy,
around us
the world has retreated,
dormant
beneath a fine mist
of ambiguous solitude,
like devious leaves
of rampant ivy,
warped shadows coil
at the edges
of our thoughts
suffocating
our mind,
time turns into echoes
echoes of time
and endless days,
filled with glaring
garish sun,
twist
into soupish murk.

Chronic Illness: Resilience Through a Never-Ending Pandemic

Emma Brimelow

Prochlorperazine, Betahistine, Cinnarizine, Cyclizine, Amitriptyline. My drawers are filled with more medication than those of an elderly woman.

In the past year, I have seen the faces of doctors more than I have seen the faces of friends.

I have cried more over my own health than I ever have about a teenage heartbreak, university stress, or even the coronavirus pandemic.

The thing about a pandemic is that it comes to an end. Social media posts regarding lockdown blues and isolation struggles will be replaced by videos of partying students, reunions with grandparents and pictures of supermarket shelves fully stocked with toilet roll. People will ditch their newly found crochet hobby for bottomless brunches, concert tickets and new job opportunities, all whilst binning their face masks and scrapping social distancing rules. Over the past year we have shown resilience through one of the most trying times we have experienced as a nation, but inevitably, it will come to an end.

For some people, that sort of resilience is required throughout their entire lives when dealing with a long-term illness. For some people, the pandemic never ends.

It took over a year for me to receive a diagnosis and proper medication all whilst dealing with the effects of the pandemic. I spent every day from November 2019 to December 2020 with debilitating vertigo (the sensation that your surroundings are moving): headaches, derealisation episodes and even sometimes feeling on the verge of fainting. I was told for over a year that it was anxiety, I was responsible for my symptoms and that 'mindfulness' would make them go away. I travelled for hours to attend hospital appointments where I was ridiculed and told that everything I was experiencing was all in my head. I lived my life feeling like I was constantly onboard a sinking ship, both metaphorically and literally, with every movement sending me spiralling into dizziness and motion sickness. Sometimes I spent weeks on end not being able to get out of bed. I had to quit my job and attending university became almost impossible.

It took filing a complaint against my healthcare provider to finally get the care I desperately needed. In December 2020 I was diagnosed with a condition called vestibular migraine and I was consequently put on medication to control my flare ups. Relief flooded my veins as I realised someone was finally taking me seriously – someone wanted to help. I felt disgusted that it took a year to get to a point of diagnosis.

When you suffer through an unknown condition for so long, you worry intensely. Is it life threatening? Will I need surgery? Will I be like this for the rest of my life? Fortunately, there are so many online forums that depict what others are also going through. I was excited to reach out to other sufferers of chronic illnesses, but when I heard stories like my own of people who were neglected by healthcare providers, it broke my heart. Did you know that on average it takes over seven years for someone with a chronic illness to be diagnosed? Did you know that on average someone will see at least eight doctors before receiving a correct diagnosis? Medical gaslighting is extremely common. Thankfully, I was lucky. I was so, so lucky.

People who live with a long-term illness must have that resilience that we faced the pandemic with for the rest of their lives. Once the pandemic ends and everything goes back to 'normal', some people still must face every day knowing that their illness may cancel their plans or send them to the E.R. Instead of Boris Johnson telling them that pubs are closed, they are the ones texting their friends that they cannot make it due to pain or fatigue. Instead of an international travel ban stopping them from visiting their dream countries, some must accept the fact that they'll never be able to travel with their health condition; or if they can, that it will be an extremely uncomfortable experience. Personally, I was grateful for the pandemic, as were many others. Whilst I was missing out on what were meant to be the best years of my life – so was everyone else. I would not have to sit at home watching my friends' snapchat stories at university Freshers' events because there simply wasn't any.

It was refreshing to see an influx of social media support towards those suffering with being homebound or in isolation. Celebrities and influencers began posting daily about mental health, surviving the pandemic, and sharing their own struggles to help raise awareness. Everyone has come together regarding mental health through the pandemic and understands how much of a toll isolation can take on a person. The government even appointed Dr Alex George as the country's mental health ambassador – a position which never existed until the pandemic began.

I respect each person who has spoken up about mental health during this time, however I want to question... where was it before the pandemic? Where was this support when thousands of people were struggling with mental health prior to 2020? Will this support continue after the pandemic? After the first news of life returning to 'normal', my social media timelines are already being taken over by harmful posts about dieting for a summer body, and how people just can't wait to get to the pub on the 21st June. At the time of writing this it has been four days since the government announced their roadmap out of the pandemic and already, I have noticed that posts about mental health have vanished.

People with chronic illnesses must live with the fact that whilst everything opens back up again, their world remains as closed off as ever. For them, 21st June is just another day. For them, the only excitement comes from knowing healthcare will slowly become easier to access. Whilst they watch everyone return to work, school, sport etc. some of them remain stuck inside waiting for their flare up to calm down enough to allow them to get out of bed and shower.

I am extremely lucky to have more good days than bad days, however for some, their entire lives revolve around being too ill to do anything but the bare minimum. This cannot always be helped, but the awareness around it can.

Mental health awareness will slowly deteriorate as we ease out of the pandemic and there will not be nearly enough support for those who need it. Over the past year we have all been reminded to check up on our friends and family, look after each other, and support people who are unable to access things like groceries and doctors' appointments etc. However, once we return to 'normal', there will still be so many people suffering who need our help. Check in with your friends who are flaring up, making them unable to leave the house. Check in with your friends who are immunodeficient and are still unable to risk going outside. Check in with your friends who struggle so much with their depression/anxiety/PTSD that they are still unable to go and get their food shopping. These people are living through their very own pandemic every single day and often feel alone, helpless and ignored.

Not only are they ignored, but they are often ridiculed by society. Many chronic illnesses are invisible and can result in someone being discriminated against in public. That seemingly normal girl you work with that uses the disabled toilets? She could have Crohn's disease and need to use a colostomy bag. Your student who often turns up late could have chronic fatigue syndrome and have dragged themselves out of bed at their lowest just to make it to your class. That seemingly drunk woman struggling to walk you laughed at on the street could be suffering from chronic vertigo and be petrified of leaving the house in fear that she will fall. Telling your friend whose disability prevents them from working that they're lucky is just as bad as discrimination. They don't have the privilege to pursue their dream job. As a society, we need to stop assuming that everyone is as able-bodied as we are.

There are so many ways to help people suffering with chronic illnesses, whether that be offering to visit them for a movie night when they're not up to going to the cinema or picking up their groceries when they aren't well enough to leave the house. Even just a small message asking how they're coping can make such a big difference. It's so easy to fall back into normality once lockdown ends, but even a small gesture like checking in with a friend that you know struggles physically or mentally can make such a big difference. The end of the pandemic doesn't mean the end of people being isolated, and it shouldn't mean the end of support for people's mental health either. As a society, we can do better.

Eat, Sleep, Repeat

Elizabeth Colcombe

Food, for me, is a constant pleasure: I like to think greedily about it, reflect deeply on it, learn from it; it provides comfort, inspiration, meaning and beauty as well as sustenance and structure.
– Nigella Lawson

I tend to pinpoint memories through the food which was at the centre of those moments. One of the earliest memories I have is my fifth birthday. It was in our local pub and play-area where most of my childhood birthday parties were held; with its sticky patterned carpets and an 'adults only' section with the occasional tease of flashing lights from the fruit machines. The only thing I can remember was staining my favourite pink t-shirt, which had frilled sleeves and a vinyl print of a Dalmatian, sitting pretty in the centre with a bow balancing on its ear. I was enjoying my pub-classic chocolate fudge cake, microwaved so the thick icing would melt and mask the dryness from its previous frozen state, until I realised I had smudged it all down my front. I remember crying because my Mum told me that chocolate stains and we wouldn't be able to get it out in the wash. As an adult who has been doing her own washing, and subsequent chocolate eating for many years now, I can confirm it does come out in the wash. The t-shirt probably needed throwing out due to over-wear or even out growing it, so this was a good excuse, but the experience of it all smeared the memory on me like the stain. Aside from this traumatic recollection, I view food as art, rather than a necessity to sustain my structure of flesh and bones. Much like the scene in *Ratatouille*, where the flavours take the form of songs and colours which dance and harmonise around the head of a rat, I imagine that's what my outer aura would look like. That is, if Disney ever wanted to make this piece into a new Princess movie; one who eats, sleeps and cries all day during a global pandemic.

I save, share, like, follow and interact with so many different food accounts on Instagram as a way to scout local places for me to try next. One of my favourite accounts right now is the new vegan kebab shop which opened down the road from the student house I can't return to. 'Home' is an unchanging rural village which has one classic, greasy takeaway and the same public transport it had when public transport was invented. Cut off from the contemporary world in advanced travel and decent food, which is why I stare at the beautifully constructed plant-based Instagram posts, while I eat my 70p noodles in the middle of the night. I love eating professionally constructed food, as they generally know more about what they're doing than I do, but I also love to cook. However, I'm incapable of following a recipe to the exact measurement or ingredient. I blame my grandparents for letting me make fake meals for them by experimenting with all the spices and nearly expired food; throwing it around into pans which were placed on an unlit stove and balancing on the edge of a chair, pushed right up to the countertop. I still just chuck things about and throw in what feels right, and it always turns out fine; it's just nothing like Jamie Oliver intended when he wrote the unopened cookbook sat on my shelf.

As I'm writing this, we're in our third national lockdown, with Boris Johnson's attempt at "third time's the charm" when protecting the country. A year of lockdowns, tiers and social distancing has made food go from a hobby to a faraway fantasy. Instead of scrolling my Instagram to find new places to visit, I'm heading downstairs for my fifth double decker before it's even 3pm. There is the odd day where me and my boyfriend, Jacob, want to construct an elaborate meal which takes longer than 10 minutes to make. As we endure the same week we've had since last March, we like to try and break it up with food which doesn't come pre-made out of the freezer. Those days are a nice relief, as lockdown has given me the time to spend on more complex recipes I wouldn't have usually attempted. Before the pandemic, life between work and university was thirty-minute bursts of "me time" where I'd shove something down to stop my stomach from crying. Each lockdown Jacob's parents always welcome me into their "one household". In the first one there was me, Jacob, his parents and a Tunisian lodger called Aymen who was here for work but got trapped. Now, in our third one, there's no Aymen, but we gained Jacob's Grandparents. With the number of us, mealtimes feel like a dinner party or some kind of awkward family event where most of the guests didn't show up. Every night is like an episode of Come Dine with Me, in which a different person presents their creations to the rest of us. Though, we do often cheat and suggest a takeaway; those nights will always get a 10/10 from me.

The bestseller ads that Amazon uses to try and coax me into buying the things everyone else is, have made it obvious that the current situation has also given others the time to appreciate the role of food in life. Obviously it works, especially in a Lockdown where there's nothing else to do but buy overpriced post-it notes with fancy flower borders; or Japanese treats which will inevitably be disgusting, because you bought them from Amazon, and the product picture looks like it's been taken on a webcam. There has been heavy promotion of books like *In the Kitchen: Essays on Food and Life*, Nigella's new piece *Cook, Eat, Repeat*, and even Stanley Tucci, an amazing actor and curator of online, quarantine cocktail tutorials, has published *My Life Through Food*. I've bought all of them because I'm shamelessly a slave to the Amazon recommended ads. Everyone seems to be interested in food on a personal level above the sustainable properties it's intended to have. I thought my biggest breakthrough as a writer would be some kind of food writing where I wrote stories alongside the recipes and have some ground-breaking new form for people to obsess over. However, my wish lists, and years of other foodie writers, say otherwise. Amazon was yet to tell me this form already existed, so I'm new to the world of food writing and the books Nigella had already crafted in my 'ground-breaking' style. Like her *Cook, Eat, Repeat*, If I was to write my own recipe book on the food habits of my Lockdown, *Eat, Sleep, Repeat* would be a more appropriate title.

There are so many food stories that have happened throughout the pandemic which would go into this *Eat, Sleep, Repeat* memoir. I never used to have time to be so eccentric with something we had to fit in between the 'more important' things we had going on in our busy lives. Like the dalgona coffee some adolescent made a tutorial out of, renaming the traditional South Korean drink the 'Tiktok coffee'; something which me and Jacob spent at least fifteen minutes making every other day, because what else did we have to do at 2 pm when we would undoubtably have just woken up. On one of the many days where I was trying to procrastinate my assignments, I decided to dedicate myself in recreating the traditional cinnamon buns I used to eat in Stockholm. When I was making them, I orchestrated a photograph of myself, making Jacob take it to look candid. In an old yellow t-shirt and some jeans which I couldn't button up anymore. Smiling like I hadn't gotten dressed and put a bit of make up on just for that. Twisting homemade dough into small knots, to show my social media I hadn't completely succumbed to the lockdown slob; even though I undeniably put my ripped leggings I've had since I was 17 back on, seconds after the photo was taken. Even the countless loaves of bread Jacob's Dad, and the rest of the country began making each day, warranted a recording. He dusted off an old bread maker out of the garage, but it could only knead and proof the dough as the cooking function had died along with the people who probably created it. He built up a bulk store of flour in the utility room as a result of the supermarkets experiencing 'panic buying' of essentials. A new loaf of bread was made and eaten in the same day, every day; the panic buying quickly died down, bread, toilet roll, and eggs returned to shops, but the two stone of carbohydrate weight I put on didn't move. I wrote a list of food experiences I've had during this pandemic in the back of my journal. Pinpointing specific moments which were quickly moulding into one another, for the *Sleep, Eat, Repeat* piece I'll probably never write. The contents of the list will soon just be another memory, filed away with my pink Dalmatian trauma, and a faint memorial to Tucci's cocktail videos.

The Magic of the Unknown

Nicole Frankel

I was 18 years old, studying in my second year of A-Levels. In English Literature, we were learning about gothic fiction. So far, I had been disappointed to learn that *Dracula* was nothing like *Twilight* and Disney had lied about fairy tale endings.

During one lesson, our teacher told us to go around the room and share our greatest fears; it was strangely personal information to share in class. My muscles tensed as my body screamed *run!* Firstly, because I'd dreaded speaking in front of people for as long as I could remember. Secondly, because I'd rather shave off my eyebrows than reveal my greatest fear.

The most common answers were spiders, snakes and clowns. Even though I knew it wasn't that simple, I couldn't help but wish that my fear was something that could be so easily avoided. The closer it got to my turn, the faster my heart raced. I knew I could just make something up, but the harder I tried not to think about my fear, the more I thought about it.

Then we got to my friend, who said that her biggest fear was the unknown.

Oooh.

Our teacher nodded in approval.

It was the first abstract answer, something you couldn't easily get a fix on. I gratefully latched onto this and gave it as my answer without incident, even though this fear hadn't yet made it onto my list. After, I felt inexplicably guilty for not being honest. Even though I knew that no one cared, I still felt like I'd somehow cheated.

But looking back, I realise that my answer was technically true. Doesn't the unknown underpin everything we're afraid of? We're either afraid that something will happen, or that it won't. Fear manifests in the present, but really, it's about the future.

If 18-year-old me had been able to see what was coming for her then, well, there's a reason that humans don't possess the ability to see into the future. But she wasn't afraid of the unknown, because she had a plan. Now, I'm not saying that you shouldn't make plans, but if you do, don't become too attached to them. Since I finished my A-Levels, absolutely nothing in my life has turned out as I expected, or would have chosen if life gave us that option. For the next few years, I watched my friends leave me behind as they moved out, got married, started careers. When I let myself, I wondered if those things would ever happen to me. The uncertainty of the future followed me like a shadow, always reminding me that I had no idea what was going to happen.

Fast forward to 2020 at the start of the pandemic, which brought with it a host of uniquely individual challenges. I saw people who I'd always been jealous of, really struggle. What surprised me about this is that I realised that I was okay. Me, who I'd always considered weak; who never seemed able to deal with the things in life that didn't seem to bother other people. But I was okay – content even.

I haven't admitted this to anyone because it feels wrong. I feel guilty about feeling okay in a situation that is anything but.

But what other choice do we have?

Sure, there are things I wish I could do. I am counting down the days until I can finally do the WAP dance in a club! Despite things not being perfect, I feel at peace, possibly more so than I've ever felt. Now I realise that those years of living in fear of the future, of the unknown, have prepared me to face this year of collective uncertainty. It's a cliché, but despite the suffering, now I'm grateful because for me, this experience is nothing new. I have discovered a reserve of strength that I didn't know I possess. But perhaps more importantly, I've found inner peace in the chaos.

Last year I started studying a completely new degree and, ironically, for the first time in my life I find myself not being afraid of the future, but instead looking forward to it. Because the magical thing about the unknown is that it represents potential. Anything can happen, and it might be bad, but it could also be great – greater than you could ever dream. And that's what I choose to focus on.

Nothing's really changed. The future remains unknown, but there are two things I know with certainty. The first one is that I have no idea what's going to happen. The second, is that whatever happens, I'll be okay.

Resilience Through the Unknown: Reflections on a Global Pandemic

Cassie Harrison

What does it mean to be resilient?
How does this manifest in our endurance of the unknown?

Resilience refers to our ability to persevere, and bounce back, regardless of hardship. This capacity for tenacity and elasticity may be perceived as elusive and ambitious, yet it relies on simplicity. That is, the fundamentals of well-being, often overlooked in times of crisis. For example, a global pandemic.

STAYING GROUNDED

Any event that induces stress or fear can trigger our fight-or-flight response. This causes our sympathetic nervous system to release hormones into our bloodstream, activating physiological responses, such as increased heart rate and quickened breathing (Harvard Health Publishing). Unexpected challenges can therefore leave us with an abundance of energy and darting flights of thought that can be all-consuming. But, staying grounded can help us to overcome this.

When the pandemic began, I remember the first time I witnessed the results of stockpiling. Not through a screen, but at my local supermarket. The empty shelves I saw before me made it real. After the breaking news of school closures, I remember saying goodbye to my students, not knowing when I would see them again. It became my job to console them, and their concerned families. I remember the first time the virus affected somebody I knew – a young father, hospitalised, and placed on a ventilator. At such difficult times, it was my composure that got me through.

Reigniting my self-belief, previously clouded by fear. I remind myself, *"I can cope." "This won't last forever."*

I eliminate unhelpful media consumption. Unsubscribe. Unfriend. Unfollow.

Pause. Take three deep breaths. In then out. Slowly.

I awaken my senses by identifying three red artefacts, five sounds and two textures that are present in my surroundings.

A mindful retreat from anxious thoughts.

STAYING CONNECTED

Prolonged activation of the physiological responses associated with stress can cause ongoing anxiety, and other mental health issues. Sudden shifts in routines and expectations can also take a toll on our mental health. For example, being required to work or study from home, home-school our children, deal with sudden loss – of our freedom, of loved ones.

The pandemic had an impact on us all. We faced the same uncertainties. And yet, no two people found themselves in identical circumstances. Whatever hardships you face, others will also have encountered, but your situation will remain unique to you.

Our support network becomes more crucial than ever. We need to talk, to seek help, to empathise, to be there for others, to manage perceptions. We need to inform others of our evolving situation, and be aware of that of those around us.

Resilience is a collaborative effort. We all deserve support.

STAYING PRESENT

External chaos can evoke feelings of hopelessness and powerlessness. But, focusing on the things that we can control and nurturing our internal selves, increases our resilience in the face of uncertainty.

I maintain a sense of purpose by aiming to achieve three things each day. Sometimes my goals will be trivial – take a walk, paint my nails, change the bed sheets, finish my book. At other times, I'll challenge myself with heavy duty tasks, such as cleaning the oven, completing an assignment or running errands I've delayed for weeks. We can be kind to ourselves by taking this day-by-day approach – hour by hour, on some occasions.

Prioritise. Don't let a day go by without breathing fresh air, moving your body, consuming your vitamins. Refrain from fixating on the lives and actions beyond your own – don't permit the negative energies of others to invade your mental space.

Resilience requires us to *show up* for ourselves, in any way we can. Now.

Practicing gratitude is another way to embrace the present. This is choosing a positive mindset. Consider the legend of two wolves, at battle, within us. One wolf is evil, and encompasses our unhealthy thoughts, such as jealousy, self-pity and resentment. The other, is good, and consists of positive notions – love, peace, humility, empathy, generosity. This leads us to question which wolf wins the internal battle. Always the one we feed, is the answer.

Thus, consciously adopting a positive outlook allows good thoughts to prevail. At times this can be difficult, though we can start small, by making a mental note of things that we are grateful for in any day, or moment. Right now, I am grateful that I have a spacious and comfortable place to work. I am grateful for the cool glass of clean water I have beside me. I am also grateful for the fresh herbs that are thriving on my windowsill. I love the greenery in my home, their scent, the distinct flavours they add to my cooking. I am grateful that I can use writing as a means of self-expression and reflection. I could go on.

Blessings are like stars – injecting light and magic into our lives – but also in the way that they multiply when you pay them attention. When we pause, and look up into the night's sky, we first notice one star, soon followed by another, and another. They proliferate. I urge you to try it – both counting stars, and counting your blessings.

While we have control over our day-to-day lives, other things are beyond our control. We can be present in the moment, and accept that there are things we cannot control. Maintaining a realistic perspective in this way enhances our resilience.

In *The Power of Now*, Eckhart Tolle insists that we must "Surrender to what *is*." (28) explaining that, "…the more you are able to honour and accept the Now, the more you are free of pain, of suffering" (27). Coming to terms with our hardships, as opposed to dwelling on them, will increase our ability to bounce back.

REFLECTION

When faced with any kind of setback, seeking meaning from our experience is part of our recovery journey. We can explore our innermost thoughts through creative endeavours, such as art, journaling or writing. Though communication with those around us, and internal reflection, is also enough. Glennon Doyle, in *Untamed*, notes the importance of looking inwards, suggesting that we must uncover in order to recover. This exemplifies the value of honing in on the positive outcomes of a situation. Reflection often enables us to see things from a new perspective.

Like others, I was struck by the hardships of the pandemic. I began grieving for the first time. I ardently missed my friends and family. I lost my job. But, I learnt new things…

Despite my feelings of rejection when my full-time teaching contract wasn't renewed, thoughtful reflection led me to recognise that there were alternative industries to explore. My resilience enabled me to seek opportunities to exercise my passion in writing. And now, my day-to-day life is fulfilling and exciting, rather than exhausting and hopeless. I no longer live for the weekends.

I also no longer spend £5 on coffee that I can make at home, because those fivers add up.

Whenever I can, I'll now do my shopping in store, rather than online. I'll interact with the shop assistants, and may even accept a hand massage from the kind people in Lush, without feeling awkward. I'll allow myself to be inspired by the aesthetic displays of products. I'll try on the dress flaunted by the mannequin. Maybe I'll also buy the jewellery accentuating it.

I'll not put off cocktail evenings with my friends in favour of spending all seven nights of the week on the sofa in my pyjamas.

I will hug my family a little tighter, a little longer.

Unearth the positives, hone in on what you have learnt, allow the challenges to encourage you to make changes you didn't know you needed to make.

Perhaps, over the past year, you have inadvertently applied these strategies in your endurance of the unknown, and have been more resilient than you realise. These methods of resilience are universal. They can support the well-being of anyone, at any time. Whatever challenges we face – loneliness, loss, disaster, illness, conflict, financial hardship – how we process these changes and events will determine the impact they have on us in the long-term.

References:

· Doyle, Glennon. *Untamed: Stop pleasing, start living.* The Dial Press, 2020.
· Harvard Health Publishing. *Understanding the stress response.* Harvard Health Publishing, 2011. health.harvard.edu/staying-healthy/understanding-the-stress-response. Accessed 4 Mar. 2021.
· Tolle, Eckhart. *The Power of Now: A Guide to Spiritual Enlightenment.* Hodder and Stoughton, 1999.

Joined at the Lip

Jayne Stead

Today, we discover you have lost something of yourself.

The gap in your face has been there since we first saw you. Grainy and almost imperceptible on the scan. Kidney shaped and, with some wriggling and poking, your face has turned and there is the shadow. The hole that will be. There are the dark, granular sockets of your face where the eyes are, but they are expected.

Not so below.

Where your nose is, a curved crescent moon of a line drops and darkens. An absence. Of course, we only see this when the sonographer points this out to us. She has gone silent. She pushes harder into my skin on the extended dome of you and me. Getting a better look. Then, her voice cracks as she tells us there is something wrong. Something missing. She suspects a harelip she says. She wants a second opinion. She brings in another nurse. Older, wiser. An air of competence and no nonsense fills the room pushing our frightened glances to the walls. What? What? We want to urge them to speak to us, but we know this is serious, that these two women hold some control over our happiness in their hands. What they need to do is concentrate and get it right. We let them. Until finally, the senior of the two turns to us and says: "I'm sorry". She explains that they have detected a cleft lip and that she is very certain, and again she apologises. We both know exactly what that is and in a direct contrast to the barely veiled dismay of the two medical professionals in the room we think, "Thank God – is that all".

What we learn in the coming months is that an alarming number of parents still terminate pregnancies because of this hole in a face. We are treated in hushed voices and comforting smiles by the specialist team we are immediately put in touch with. Everyone wants a perfect child they say. There are many scans and many consultations. We are watched and gently supported into not abandoning you. They don't seem to believe us that it never even crossed our minds. That we thought the choking back of worry and tears from hospital staff had indicated a worse condition that there was no coming back from. We are slightly amused by this and enjoy seeing your face with its fissure of shade, as we get to know you as you grow inside the safety of the womb.

We read. Of course.

We learn that babies form like the closing of a clay pot. That the last join the body stitches together is the line down the face and sometimes the messages just don't get through. The body forgets to finish it off. You are no more than a forgotten piece of embroidery. My body has not quite completed the job. We learn you are lucky, in that it is a unilateral cleft, and is only down one side of your mouth. You are unlucky, in that it is also the palate, and that this will require even more surgery and that you may have trouble speaking and need speech therapy. None of this phases us. We are sure all will be well. We have no idea if it will be.

We also learn that history has not judged facial clefts kindly. Superstition and ignorance dominate. Greeks ignored their existence, Spartans and Romans killed such children as they believed they harboured evil spirits. Horror and utter disbelief were the reactions to congenital deformities in ancient times with infants being moved from tribal communities or cultural units. Aztec mothers were advised not to observe a lunar eclipse otherwise the child would be born with a cleft. And, up until very recently in our own culture, people believed the mother's path must have been crossed by a hare for this abnormality to happen. Hence the harelip. In truth the harelip came from the shape of a hare's mouth not this, but superstition and folklore are hard to let go. No one under the age of fifty would say harelip now. Twenty years ago, no one should have either. But it still slips through. And, as I type, spellcheck acknowledges that it is a real word. No linguistic anomaly here.

When you are born, the gap is the first thing we see as you are pulled from me and held up to the cold hospital light. Your face is split, and we can see the folds of your pink mouth. We are aware we are seeing something usually unseen. It is surprising how unimportant it is, even though we know that for the next six months it will be the first thing that everyone will see. For some, it will be the only thing they will see. We set off into the unknown.

But it turns out you are blessed with an extra wide smile, one that reaches your eyes and a formidable giggle. That gap becomes you. You are not defined by it. It just is. We are fearless in parading you out and about. What is normal to us has become normal to others as we welcome stares, questions and enjoy explaining. Strangers look on and smile, not one person says anything cruel and I, as your mother, hold tightly onto a kernel of hope this will be the case forever; hope that the playground will be kind and friends will wait to hear what you are wanting to say. But that is all ahead of us yet.

For now, we navigate feeding a child with milk that goes everywhere with no membranes to contain it. They give us especially designed teats to feed you. It resembles a silicone coat hook and means the milk can spurt to the back of your mouth and avoid the nose. It is designed with air holes punctured in it to aid suckling, so you don't have to rely on the tight channel of the mouth to get what you need. The bottles are also softer silicone so we can help by squeezing gently and getting the pumped breast milk to where it can do you good. It becomes easy and natural, and we become experts and we are proud. Of ourselves, of you. We have some of those teats left after all these years. They are in the back of a drawer, have survived a house move and we come across them when we are least expecting to and show them to each other. Holding one in an unfurling palm like a gift from the past. Slightly sheepish we indulge ourselves. Sometimes we shed a tear at how far you have come, how brave you have been. Sometimes we just murmur, "do you remember....". They are sticky now with the rubber degrading, tacky to the touch. Our eyes meet and the shared memory is ours alone. It seems like a lifetime ago. A mixture of love and weariness of joy and anxiety. We cannot begin to even think of throwing them away. They get returned to the drawer until they will be unearthed again – turned over into our lives like soil cleaved by the plough.

A cleft in the lip is usually mended at three months. The palate later. Mr Henley, the surgeon, will be cutting you down the folds of your divided lip and intricately stitching them together. Sinew and nerves. Like darning a sock from the inside out. Mr Henley has hands like hams. He plays rugby and has a ruddy face. We cannot imagine how such hands can do such delicate work, but we know he is one of the best this country has to offer, and we feel safe. He talks to you beautifully, with great care and notices every muscle on your face. We laugh heartily at his bad jokes so he will work the hardest with you above all others.

The day you are 'mended' is one of fear and trepidation for us. Not as you might think from the operation itself – more that the boy who we know, Benjamin (chosen with no s's no f's no t's) is about to go. The hole we have grown to know and work with, cherish and worry about will be no more and we can't help but think we are losing you. A part of you. Something that was never actually there. We cannot help ourselves and when it comes to passing you to the anaesthetist in the theatre, she has to firmly prise you from your father's arms, all the time reassuring us and getting us brave enough to leave.

We go.

The hours pass as we sit by an empty cot on the ward, and we wait to meet you all over again.

York Centre for Writing
Creative Writing Schools Competition

This year, 2021, was the inaugural year of the York Centre for Writing Creative Writing Schools competition. This had been planned for some months ahead of schedule but just as the information was about to be sent out to schools and colleges the first lockdown was called. The sudden isolation that this caused gave us the theme for entries: *bringing people together*. Open to all schools and colleges internationally, entrants could submit a poem, monologue, short story or essay. These are the winners!

Hope

Ahmad Umar Tanvir Kadri
(St. Joan of Arc International School,
Tiruchirappalli, Tamil Nadu, India · Age: 17 years)

Now the world is depending on hope,
Let's join all together to become its rope.

Let's take up the resolution,
To save the next generation.

Let's not cut the tree,
And leave our animals free.

I have a hope,
That we are going to cope.

Don't depress,
B'cause, you have more to impress.

Keep up the smile,
B'cause you have the journey of miles.

The Race for Christmas

Louise Sawyer
(Greenhead College, Year 13)

It was Christmas Eve afternoon. The twins, Christopher and Catherine, were at choir practice, rehearsing for the Carol Concert that evening. They were singing a verse of 'Away in a Manger' when suddenly the organ made a funny noise. The Organist frowned and pressed the key again.

BARP!

The Organist shook his head. "I need to fix this before tonight or the Carol Concert will be cancelled. Kit and Kat can you go to the Hardware shop for a 20cm bolt for me please."

Christopher and Catherine nodded. "Yes, of course. The Carol Concert can't be cancelled. It won't be Christmas without it."

Kit and Kat put on their hats and scarves and went outside. Big, fat flakes of snow were falling.

They walked through the snow to the small shop in the village centre.

"Hello Mr. Hardware." Said Kit "Do you have a 20cm bolt for the church organ please? It's broken. If it isn't fixed the concert will be cancelled and it won't be Christmas."

The Hardware man looked in his big box of bolts. "I'm sorry Kit and Kat, these bolts are all different sizes and I can't measure them because my ruler has snapped. I'll give you the bolt for free if you can fetch me a ruler from the Newsagents. I'm looking forward to the Carol Concert."

So off they went to the Newsagents.

"Hello Mrs. Newsagent, do you have a ruler for Mr. Hardware so he can measure a bolt to fix the organ please? It's broken. If it isn't fixed the concert will be cancelled and it won't be Christmas."

"Okay." The Newsagent said. "I'll find a ruler if you can fetch me a sandwich for my lunch from the Bakers. I'll give you the ruler for free if you do. The Carol Concert must happen!"

So off they went to the Bakers.

"Hello Mr. Baker, do you have a sandwich for Mrs. Newsagent please? She's finding a ruler for Mr. Hardware so he can measure a bolt to fix the organ. It's broken. If it isn't fixed the concert will be cancelled and it won't be Christmas."

"The Newsagent likes chicken sandwiches." The Baker said. "But I've run out of chicken. If you fetch me some from the Butcher I'll give you the sandwich for free. I've been practicing my singing for the concert all morning."

So off they went to the Butcher.

"Hello Mrs. Butcher, do you have some chicken for Mr. Baker so he can make a sandwich for Mrs. Newsagent please? She's finding a ruler for Mr. Hardware so he can measure a bolt to fix the organ. It's broken. If it isn't fixed the concert will be cancelled and it won't be Christmas."

"Yes Kit and Kat, here is the chicken for the Baker." The Butcher said. "I was just about to take it. If you take it for me I'll give it you for free. I'll see you at the concert."

Kit and Kat took the chicken to the Baker.

"Thank you Kit and Kat. Here is the sandwich for the Newsagent."

They took the sandwich to the Newsagent.

"Here is your sandwich. It's chicken."

"My favourite! Thank you." replied the Newsagent "Here is the ruler for the Hardware man."

They took the ruler to the Hardware man.

"Here is your ruler."

"Thank you." The Hardware man measured his bolts. "Found one! Here is a 20cm bolt."

They took the bolt to the Organist.

"Fantastic! Thank you Kit and Kat." smiled the Organist. He went to mend the organ.

Soon the church was filled with music. Kit and Kat cheered. The choir clapped. Choir practice began again.

The Christmas Eve Carol Concert wasn't cancelled. Kit and Kat, stood in the choir, could see everyone sitting in the church. In the front row sat 4 special guests, Mr. Hardware, Mrs. Newsagent, Mr. Baker and Mrs. Butcher. Kit and Kat smiled at them as the choir sang 'We wish you a Merry Christmas.'

"Thank you everyone for saving Christmas!" shouted Kit and Kat. "Merry Christmas!"

Claps

Ayesha Waseem
(Wyke 6th Form College, Year 13)

Claps fill the atmosphere on Thursday eve
Thousands sign up to provide some repose
Hearts ache at night when we our freedom drive
Guilt drowning, how frivolous are these woes

When mothers are losing children daily
When the hands of struggling lovers go limp
Will it clear or forever be hazy
Or will our leader continue to skimp

As days get warmer we the pain forget
Once again we laugh and live and pretend
Now winter returns, it's not over yet
Let's come together, this isn't the end

We're stronger, smarter, and kinder perhaps
So lend a hand, smile, can you hear the claps?

Acknowledgements

EDITORIAL AND PRODUCTION TEAM

Liliana Baldanza, William Stewart, Michael Ayre,
Elisabeth Blood, Emma Cairns, Hayley Revell, Hazel Devey,
Lucy Ann Cummings, Rachel Alexander, Cheyenne Uustal

MARKETING AND BLOGS TEAM

Nathaniel Foley, Bethan Teale, Fritha MacLeod, Rachel Carter,
Julia Banaszek, Jasmine Barber, Jasmin Brier, Poppy Halliday,
Emily Oldroyd, Hannah Cross, Briony McNair

EVENTS AND PODCASTING TEAM

Leah Figiel, Luke Miles, Amie Watts, Jack Taggart, Lizzy Harrison

COVER DESIGN

Seline Layla Duzenli

'BEYOND THE WALLS' ILLUSTRATION

Katy Rose